4B

PRIMARY MATHEMATICS
Standards Edition

WORKBOOK

Marshall Cavendish
Education

D1210855

Original edition published under the title Primary Mathematics Workbook 4B Parts One and Two
© 1983 Curriculum Planning & Development Division, Ministry of Education, Singapore
Published by Times Media Private Limited

This edition © 2008 Marshall Cavendish International (Singapore) Private Limited
© 2014 Marshall Cavendish Education Pte Ltd

Published by Marshall Cavendish Education
Times Centre, 1 New Industrial Road, Singapore 536196
Customer Service Hotline: (65) 6213 9688
US Office Tel: (1-914) 332 8888 | Fax: (1-914) 332 8882
E-mail: cs@mceducation.com
Website: www.mceducation.com

Marshall Cavendish Corporation
99 White Plains Road
Tarrytown, NY 10591
U.S.A.
Tel: (1-914) 332 8888
Fax: (1-914) 332 8882
E-mail: mcc@marshallcavendish.com
Website: www.marshallcavendish.com

First published 2008
Reprinted 2009 (twice), 2010, 2011 (twice), 2012 (twice), 2013, 2014, 2015, 2016, 2017, 2018 (twice), 2019

Primary Mathematics (Standards Edition) Workbook 4B
ISBN 978-0-7614-6998-8

Printed in Malaysia

Primary Mathematics (Standards Edition) is adapted from Primary Mathematics Workbook 4B Parts One and Two (3rd
Edition), originally developed by the Ministry of Education, Singapore. This edition contains new content developed
by Marshall Cavendish International (Singapore) Private Limited, which is not attributable to the Ministry of Education,
Singapore.

We would like to acknowledge the Project Team from the Ministry of Education, Singapore, that developed the original
Singapore Edition:
Project Director: Dr Kho Tek Hong
Team Members: Hector Chee Kum Hoong, Chip Wai Lung, Liang Hin Hoon, Lim Eng Tann,
                Rosalind Lim Hui Cheng, Ng Hwee Wan, Ng Siew Lee
Curriculum Specialists: Christina Cheong Ngan Peng, Ho Juan Beng

Our thanks to Richard Askey, Emeritus Professor of Mathematics (University of Wisconsin, Madison) and Madge Goldman,
President (Gabriella and Paul Rosenbaum Foundation), for their help and advice in the production of Primary Mathematics
(Standards Edition).

We would also like to recognize the contributions of Jennifer Kempe (Curriculum Advisor, Singapore Math Inc.®) and
Bill Jackson (Math Coach, School No. 2, Paterson, New Jersey) to Primary Mathematics (Standards Edition).

CONTENTS

8 Congruent and Symmetric Figures

Blank

EXERCISE 1

1. Write each fraction as a decimal.

(a)

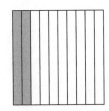

2 tenths

$$\frac{2}{10} =$$

(b)

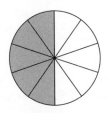

5 tenths

$$\frac{5}{10} =$$

(c)

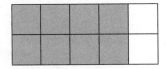

8 tenths

$$\frac{8}{10} =$$

(d)

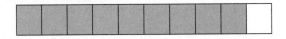

9 tenths

$$\frac{9}{10} =$$

2. What is the amount of water in liters?
   Give the answer as a decimal.

   (a)   (b)

   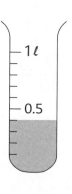   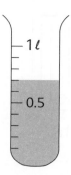

   _____ ℓ   _____ ℓ

3. What is the weight in kilograms?
   Give the answer as a decimal.

   (a)   (b)

      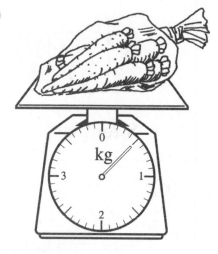

   _____ kg   _____ kg

4. Write a decimal for each of the following.

(a)
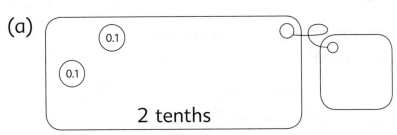
0.1   0.1   2 tenths

(b)
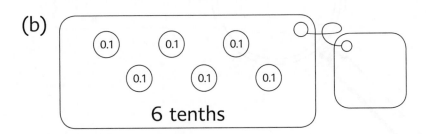
0.1   0.1   0.1   0.1   0.1   0.1   6 tenths

(c)
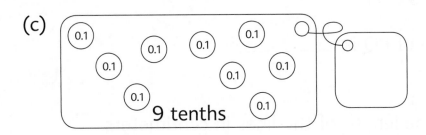
0.1   0.1   0.1   0.1   0.1   0.1   0.1   0.1   0.1   9 tenths

5. Write the missing number in each of the following.

(a)
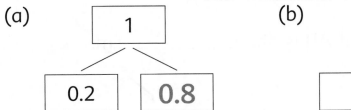
1
0.2   0.8

(b)
1
☐   0.6

(c)
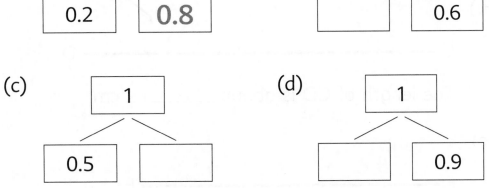
1
0.5   ☐

(d)
1
☐   0.9

EXERCISE 2

1. What is the length of PQ in centimeters?
    Give the answer as a decimal.

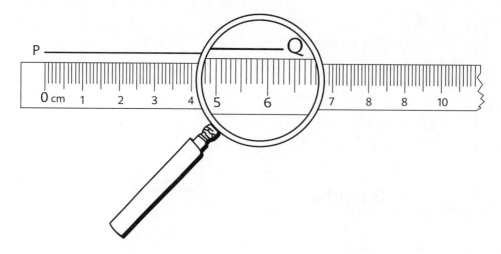

    The length of PQ is _____ cm.

2. Measure the length of the lines in centimeters.
    Give the answer as a decimal.

    (a)

    A ———————————— B

    The length of AB is about _____ cm.

    (b)

    C ———————————————— D

    The length of CD is about _____ cm.

    (c)

    E ——————————————— F

    The length of EF is about _____ cm.

3. What is the amount of water in liters?
   Give the answer as a decimal.

   (a)

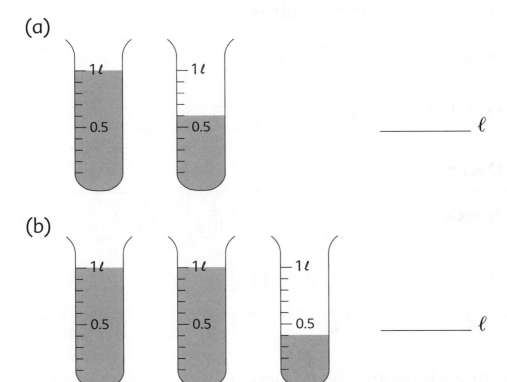

   _____ ℓ

   (b)

   _____ ℓ

4. What is the weight in kilograms?
   Give the answer as a decimal.

   (a)   (b)

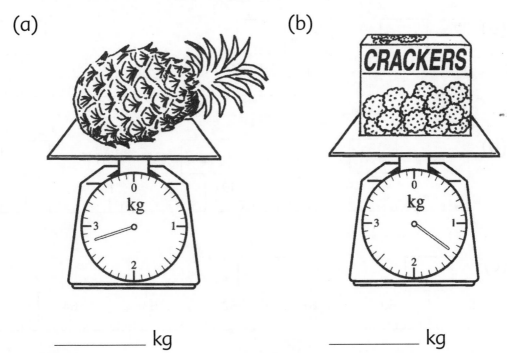

   _____ kg   _____ kg

EXERCISE 3

1. Complete the following tables.

Decimal	0.1	0.2				0.6
Fraction	$\frac{1}{10}$		$\frac{3}{10}$	$\frac{4}{10}$	$\frac{5}{10}$	

Decimal	1.1	1.2			2.2	
Fraction	$1\frac{1}{10}$		$1\frac{3}{10}$	$1\frac{4}{10}$		$3\frac{5}{10}$

2. Write each fraction as a decimal.

   (a) $\frac{4}{10}$ = ___   (b) $1\frac{4}{10}$ = ___   (c) $\frac{5}{10}$ = ___   (d) $3\frac{5}{10}$ = ___

3. Write each decimal as a fraction in its simplest form.

   (a) 0.3 = ___   (b) 2.3 = ___   (c) 0.6 = ___   (d) 3.6 = ___

4. Write the missing decimal in each box.

   (a)

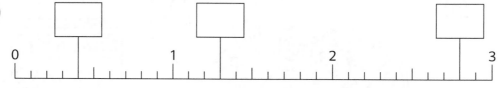

   (b)

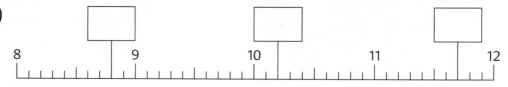

   (c)

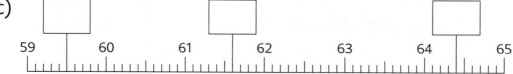

5. Write >, < or = in each ⃝.

    (a) 6.0 $\left(=\right)$ $\frac{6}{10}$ (b) 1 $\left(>\right)$ 0.1

    (c) 2.0 $\left(+\right)$ 2   (d) 5 $\left(>\right)$ 3.8

6. Circle the smallest number in each set.

    (a) 3.1,   (0.1,)   0.3,   1.3

    (b) (0.9,)   1.9,   9,   9.1

7. Circle the greatest number in each set.

    (a) 4.2,   3.2,   1.2,   (6.2)   ✓

    (b) 2.1,   (2.9,)   2,   2.4

8. Arrange the numbers in increasing order.

    7.3,   5.7,   9.6,   6.5

    <u>5.7, 6.5, 7.3, 9.6,</u>

9. Arrange the numbers in decreasing order.

    3.6,   4.9,   3.4,   9

    <u>9, 4.9, 3.6, 3.4,</u>

10. Complete the following regular number patterns.

    2.1, 2.3, 2.5, <u>2.7</u> , <u>2.9</u> , 3.1

    4.5, 5, 5.5, <u>6</u> , <u>6.5</u> , 7

EXERCISE 4

1. Write a decimal for each of the following.

    (a)

    $30 + 4 + 0.6 =$ __34.6__

    (b)

    $50 + 0.7 =$ __50.7__

    (c)

    $40 + 5 + 0.3 =$ __453__

    (d)

    $40 + 0.9 =$ __40.9__

2. Write the missing number in each box.

(a) $45.8 = 40 + 5 +$ ⬚ 0.8

(b) $70.3 = 70 +$ ⬚ 0.3

(c) $92.4 =$ ⬚ 90 $+ 2 + 0.4$

(d) $30.7 =$ ⬚ 30 $+ 0.7$

(e) $16.5 = 10 + 6 + \dfrac{⬚\,5}{10}$

(f) $60.9 = 60 + \dfrac{⬚\,9}{10}$

3. There are 12 pairs of equivalent numbers below.
   Circle each pair. (An example is shown.)

2.1	1.2	$\frac{2}{10}$	$1\frac{5}{10}$	5
0.1	$2\frac{1}{10}$	$1\frac{2}{10}$	0.5	1.5
0.3	$\frac{9}{10}$	0.9	$\frac{5}{10}$	0.8
$1\frac{3}{10}$	4.1	$4\frac{1}{10}$	$2\frac{8}{10}$	$3\frac{7}{10}$
1.3	$\frac{4}{10}$	2.8	3.7	6
0.4	1.4	$1\frac{4}{10}$	$\frac{6}{10}$	0.6

Unit 6: Decimals

EXERCISE 5

1. Write the number represented by each of the following sets of number discs.

(a)

(0.1) (0.1) (0.1) (0.1) (0.1) (0.1) (0.1) (0.1) (0.01) (0.01)	

(b)

(1) (1) (1) (0.1) (0.01) (1) (1) (1) (0.1) (0.01) (0.01) (1) (1) (0.1) (0.01)	

(c)

(1) (0.01) (0.01) (1) (1) (0.01) (0.01) (0.01)	

(d)

(1) (1) (0.01) (0.01) (1) (0.1) (0.01) (0.01) (0.01) (1) (1) (0.01) (0.01)	

(e)

(10) (0.01) (0.01) (0.01) (0.01) (0.01) (0.01) (10) (0.01) (0.01) (0.01)	

2. Write a decimal for each of the following.

(a)

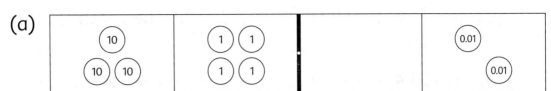

$$30 + 4 + 0.02 = \underline{\hspace{2cm}}$$

(b)

$$40 + 0.2 + 0.05 = \underline{\hspace{2cm}}$$

(c)

$$20 + 4 + 0.1 + 0.03 = \underline{\hspace{2cm}}$$

(d)

$$30 + 0.04 = \underline{\hspace{2cm}}$$

3. Fill in the blanks.

   (a) In 71.06, the digit ＿＿＿＿＿ is in the tenths place.
       Its value is ＿＿＿＿＿.

   (b) In 103.4, the digit ＿＿＿＿＿ is in the tens place.
       Its value is ＿＿＿＿＿.

   (c) In 19.**4**, the digit **4** is in the ＿＿＿＿＿ place.
       Its value is ＿＿＿＿＿.

   (d) In **5**7.01, the digit **5** is in the ＿＿＿＿＿ place.
       Its value is ＿＿＿＿＿.

   (e) In 28.6**3**, the digit **3** is in the ＿＿＿＿＿ place.
       Its value is ＿＿＿＿＿.

   (f) In 9**0**.72, the digit **0** is in the ＿＿＿＿＿ place.
       Its value is ＿＿＿＿＿.

4. Write the value of the digits in each of the following numbers.

   (a) 90.23

   (b) 87.41

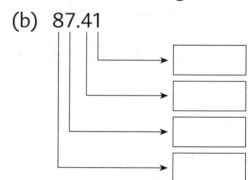

   (c) 56.09

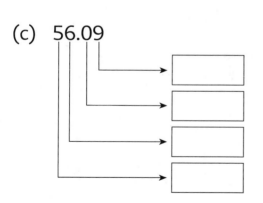

   (d) 218.8

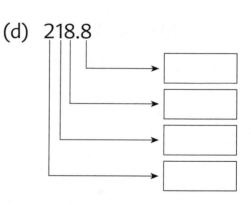

EXERCISE 6

1. Write each fraction as a decimal.

(a) 7 hundredths $\dfrac{7}{100} =$	(b) 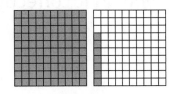 1 whole 7 hundredths $1\dfrac{7}{100} =$
(c) 58 hundredths $\dfrac{58}{100} =$	(d) 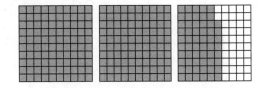 2 wholes 58 hundredths $2\dfrac{58}{100} =$
(e) $\dfrac{24}{100} =$	(f) $1\dfrac{24}{100} =$
(g) $\dfrac{65}{100} =$	(h) $3\dfrac{65}{100} =$
(i) $\dfrac{3}{100} =$	(j) $2\dfrac{3}{100} =$
(k) $\dfrac{5}{100} =$	(l) $10\dfrac{5}{100} =$

2. Join each fraction to its equivalent decimal with a straight line.
   (An example is shown.)
   If you do it correctly, you will get 3 squares.

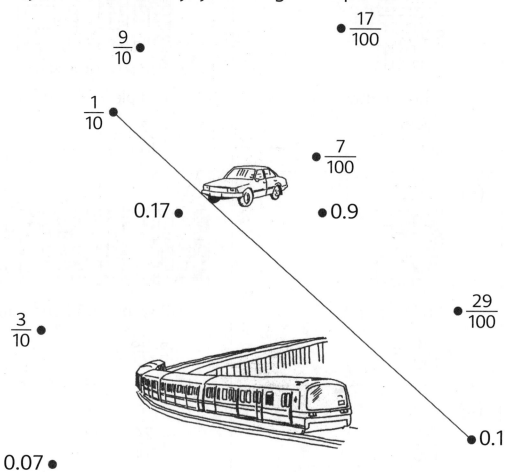

$\dfrac{17}{100}$

$\dfrac{9}{10}$

$\dfrac{1}{10}$

$\dfrac{7}{100}$

0.17

0.9

$\dfrac{3}{10}$

$\dfrac{29}{100}$

0.1

0.07

$\dfrac{7}{10}$

$\dfrac{9}{100}$

0.29

0.3

0.09

0.7

EXERCISE 7

1. Write the value of each of the following as a decimal.

    (a) $80 + \frac{7}{10} =$ _____

    (b) $20 + 4 + \frac{5}{10} =$ _____

    (c) $34 + \frac{4}{100} =$ _____

    (d) $7 + \frac{2}{10} + \frac{9}{100} =$ _____

2. Fill in the missing fractions.

    (a) $4.37 = 4 + \frac{3}{10} +$ _____

    (b) $3.05 = 3 +$ _____

    (c) $80.2 = 80 +$ _____

    (d) $1.76 = 1 +$ _____ $+ \frac{6}{100}$

    (e) $72.4 = 70 + 2 +$ _____

3. Fill in the missing decimals.

    (a) $8.24 = 8 + 0.2 +$ _____

    (b) $23.05 = 20 + 3 +$ _____

    (c) $7.14 = 7 +$ _____ $+ 0.04$

    (d) $5.08 = 5 +$ _____

    (e) $17.3 = 10 + 7 +$ _____

4. Complete the following regular number patterns.

    (a) 0.8, 0.9, _____, 1.1, _____, 1.3

    (b) 1, 1.5, 2, 2.5, _____, _____, 4

    (c) 3, 2.9, 2.8, _____, 2.6, _____, 2.4

    (d) 10, 9.5, 9, _____, 8, _____, 7

    (e) 0.05, 0.1, 0.15, _____, 0.25, _____, 0.35

    (f) 0.45, 0.4, 0.35, _____, _____, 0.2

    (g) 0.02, 0.04, 0.06, _____, 0.1, _____, 0.14

    (h) 10, 9.95, 9.9, _____, 9.8, _____, 9.7

5. Write the missing decimal in each box.

    (a)

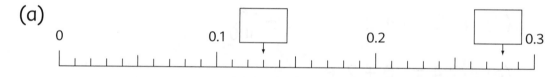

    (b)

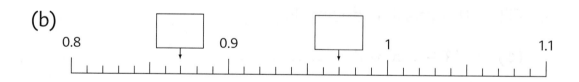

    (c)

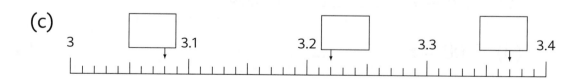

EXERCISE 8

1. Write each decimal as a fraction in its simplest form.

    (a) 0.5 = _____   (b) 2.5 = _____

    (c) 0.08 = _____   (d) 1.08 = _____

    (e) 0.15 = _____   (f) 3.15 = _____

    (g) 0.64 = _____   (h) 1.64 = _____

2. Change the denominator to 10.
    Then write the fraction as a decimal.

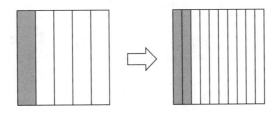

$$\frac{1}{5} = \frac{}{10} = \underline{\hspace{3cm}}$$

3. Change the denominator to 100.
    Then write the fraction as a decimal.

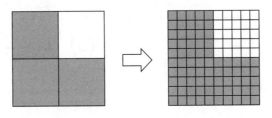

$$\frac{3}{4} = \frac{}{100} = \underline{\hspace{3cm}}$$

4. Change the denominator to 10 or 100.
Then write the fraction as a decimal.

(a) $\frac{1}{2} = \frac{}{10}$ $=$	(b) $3\frac{1}{2} = 3\frac{}{10}$ $=$
(c) $\frac{3}{5} =$	(d) $1\frac{3}{5} =$
(e) $\frac{1}{4} =$	(f) $2\frac{1}{4} =$
(g) $\frac{4}{25} =$	(h) $1\frac{4}{25} =$

5. Write each fraction as a decimal.

(a) $\frac{4}{5} =$	(b) $3\frac{4}{5} =$
(c) $\frac{9}{20} =$	(d) $1\frac{9}{20} =$
(e) $\frac{3}{50} =$	(f) $2\frac{3}{50} =$

EXERCISE 9

1. Write **>**, **<** or **=** in each ◯.

    (a)
     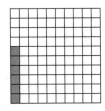

    0.4 ◯ 0.06

    (b)
       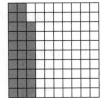

    1.3 ◯ 1.28

    (c)

    (1)(1)(1)(1)   (1)(1)(1)(1)
    (0.1)(0.1)   (0.1)(0.1)(0.1)
    (0.01)(0.01)(0.01)   (0.01)(0.01)

    4.23 ◯ 4.32

    (d)

    (1)(1)(1)(1)(1)   (1)(1)(1)
    (0.1)(0.1)(0.1)   (0.1)(0.1)(0.1)(0.1)(0.1)
                            (0.01)(0.01)(0.01)(0.01)

    5.3 ◯ 3.54

2. Write >, < or = in each ◯.

   (a) 2.01 ◯ 20.1   (b) 8.20 ◯ 0.82

   (c) 7.23 ◯ 7.3   (d) 4.9 ◯ 0.59

   (e) 1.50 ◯ 1.5   (f) 1.3 ◯ 0.13

   (g) 0.10 ◯ 0.1   (h) 5.3 ◯ 3.55

3. Circle the smallest number in each set.
   (a) 1.11,   1.2,   0.88,   2
   (b) 3.4,   2.99,   3.01,   4
   (c) 4.2,   0.99,   2.4,   0.42

4. Circle the greatest number in each set.
   (a) 2.89,   3,   2.9,   2.09
   (b) 1.76,   1.8,   8.1,   1.08
   (c) 3.09,   7.01,   5.9,   4.6

5. Arrange the numbers in decreasing order.
   (a) 6.1,   1.06,   6.01,   0.61

   _____

   (b) 5,   5.3,   5.03,   5.33

   _____

EXERCISE 10

1. Fill in the blanks.

(a)

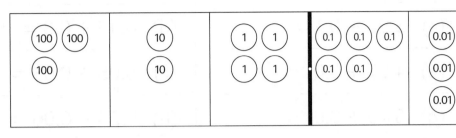

_____ is 0.01 more than 324.56.

(b)

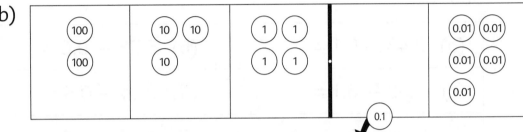

_____ is 0.1 less than 234.15.

2. Fill in the blanks.

(a) _____ is 0.1 more than 46.05.

(b) _____ is 0.01 more than 39.2.

(c) _____ is 0.1 less than 60.08.

(d) _____ is 0.01 less than 42.5.

(e) 40 is _____ more than 39.9.

(f) 32.56 is _____ more than 32.55.

(g) 52.04 is _____ less than 52.14.

(h) 65 is _____ less than 65.01.

3. Add.

(a) $5.46 + 0.1 =$	(b) $4.65 + 0.3 =$
(c) $3.92 + 0.1 =$	(d) $6.43 + 0.8 =$
(e) $4.57 + 0.01 =$	(f) $8.05 + 0.05 =$
(g) $6.49 + 0.01 =$	(h) $5.28 + 0.06 =$

4. Subtract.

(a) $2.43 - 0.1 =$	(b) $5.28 - 0.6 =$
(c) $4.08 - 0.1 =$	(d) $2.14 - 0.5 =$
(e) $3.46 - 0.01 =$	(f) $4.25 - 0.03 =$
(g) $5.2 - 0.01 =$	(h) $3.71 - 0.08 =$

5. Write the missing number in each of the following.

(a)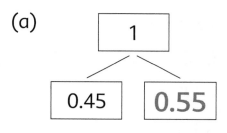

(b)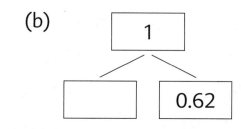

(c)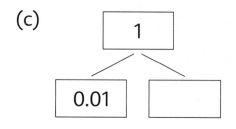

(d)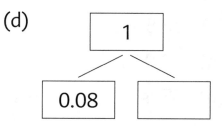

EXERCISE 11

1. Write a decimal for each of the following.

(a) (0.001) (0.001) (0.001) (0.001) 4 thousandths	
(b) (1) (1) (0.001) (0.001) (0.001) (0.001) (0.001) (1) (1) (0.001) (0.001) 4 ones 7 thousandths	
(c) (0.01) (0.01) (0.01) (0.01) (0.001) (0.001) (0.001) (0.01) (0.01) (0.01) (0.01) 8 hundredths 3 thousandths	
(d) (0.1) (0.1) (0.01) (0.01) (0.001) (0.001) (0.001) (0.1) (0.1) (0.01) (0.001) (0.001) 4 tenths 3 hundredths 5 thousandths	

2. Fill in the missing decimal in each of the following.

(a) $6.723 = 6 + 0.7 + 0.02 + $ ☐

(b) $35.406 = 35 + $ ☐

3. Fill in the missing fraction in each of the following.

(a) $9.589 = 9 + \dfrac{5}{10} + \dfrac{8}{100} + $ ☐

(b) $2.043 = 2 + $ ☐

4.

Ones		Tenths	Hundredths	Thousandths
3		**4**	**7**	**9**

Fill in the blanks.

(a) The number 3.479 is made up of _____ ones, _____ tenths, _____ hundredths and _____ thousandths.

(b) In 3.479, the digit _____ is in the tenths place. The value of the digit is _____.

(c) The value of the digit 9 is _____.

(d) The value of the digit 7 is _____.

5. Write the missing decimal in each box.

(a)
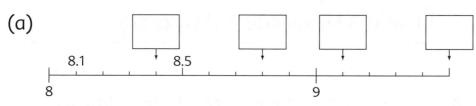

(b)
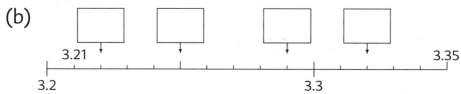

(c)
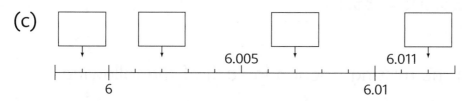

(d)
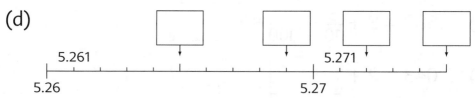

EXERCISE 12

1. Circle the greater number in each set.

    (a) 4.602,   4.7   (b) 9.1,   9.05

    (c) 1.924,   1.828   (d) 5,   0.52

2. Circle the greatest number in each set.

    (a) 24.68,   264.8,   64.82,   624.8

    (b) 5.073,   5.73,   5.307,   5.037

    (c) 0.042,   0.109,   1.1,   0.91

3. Write >, < or = in each $\bigcirc$.

    (a) 8.26 $\bigcirc$ 8.206

    (b) 7.001 $\bigcirc$ 7.1

    (c) 10.81 $\bigcirc$ 10.810

    (d) 9.345 $\bigcirc$ 9.306

    (e) 6.34 $\bigcirc$ 6.304

    (f) 6.002 $\bigcirc$ 6.200

4. Arrange the set of numbers in increasing order.

    | 2.8 | | 2.128 | | 2.18 | | 2.218 |

5. Arrange the set of numbers in decreasing order.

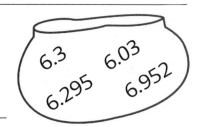

6.3   6.03
6.295   6.952

EXERCISE 13

1. Express each decimal as a fraction in its simplest form.

(a) $0.64 = \dfrac{64}{100}$ $=$	(b) $0.38 =$
(c) $2.08 =$	(d) $4.95 =$
(e) $0.216 =$	(f) $0.352 =$
(g) $3.704 =$	(h) $2.425 =$

2. Circle the greatest number in each set.

   (a) 2.5, $2\frac{1}{4}$, $2\frac{2}{5}$,   2.75

   (b) 0.127,   0.2, $\frac{3}{25}$,   0.5

   (c) 1.3, $\frac{3}{100}$,   0.9, $1\frac{1}{2}$

   (d) $\frac{1}{2}$,   0.65,   0.45, $\frac{1}{5}$

3. Arrange the numbers in increasing order.

   (a) 1.524,   1.245,   1.425,   1.254

   _____

   (b) 0.91,   0.19,   0.119,   0.097

   _____

   (c) $3\frac{1}{2}$,   3.95, $1\frac{9}{10}$ 2.5

   _____

   (d) $7\frac{1}{5}$,   7.5, $7\frac{3}{5}$,   7.1

   _____

EXERCISE 14

1. Fill in the blanks.

   (a)

   73.7 is _____ when rounded to the nearest whole number.

   (b)

   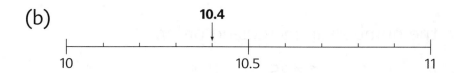

   10.4 is _____ when rounded to the nearest whole number.

   (c)

   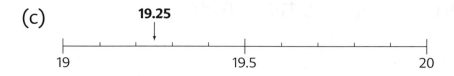

   19.25 is _____ when rounded to the nearest whole number.

   (d)

   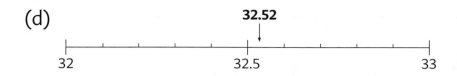

   32.52 is _____ when rounded to the nearest whole number.

2.

(a)	Ryan weighs 46.9 lb. Round his weight to the nearest pound.	
(b)	A rope is 2.5 m long. Round the length to the nearest meter.	
(c)	Sally drinks 1.25 ℓ of water a day. Round the amount of water to the nearest liter.	
(d)	The distance between Town A and Town B is 29.38 km. Round this distance to the nearest kilometer.	

3. Round each of the following to the nearest dollar.

(a)

$3.15

_____

(b)

$10.99

_____

4. Round each of the following to the nearest liter.

(a)

1.92 ℓ

_____

(b)

2.28 ℓ

_____

5. Round each of the following to the nearest whole number.

(a) 39.8 _____

(b) 46.4 _____

(c) 6.39 _____

(d) 5.92 _____

(e) 101.5 _____

(f) 299.5 _____

EXERCISE 15

1. Fill in the blanks.

   (a)

   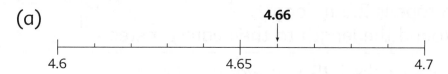

   4.66 is _____ when rounded to 1 decimal place.

   (b)

   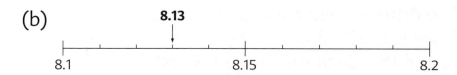

   8.13 is _____ when rounded to 1 decimal place.

2. (a)	The capacity of a teapot is 1.45 ℓ. Round the capacity to 1 decimal place.
(a)	The capacity of a teapot is 1.45 ℓ. Round the capacity to 1 decimal place.	
(b)	A package weighs 20.25 kg. Round the weight to 1 decimal place.	
(c)	A string is 9.08 m long. Round the length to 1 decimal place.	

3. The table below shows the weights of 3 children in kilograms.
   Round the weights to 1 decimal place.

Child	Weight	Rounded to 1 decimal place
A	34.91 kg	
B	41.68 kg	
C	39.75 kg	

REVIEW 6

1. Which one of the following numbers has the digit **4** in the hundreds place?

    92,**4**05, 24,905, **4**9,250, 50,9**4**2

    _____

2. In 12**5**,364, the digit **5** is in the ⬚ place.

3. Write the next number in the following regular number pattern.

    26,495,   31,495,   36,495,   41,495,   ⬚

4. Write the missing number in each of the following.

    (a) 56,180 = 50,000 + ⬚ + 100 + 80

    (b) 40,000 + 2000 + 90 + 6 = ⬚

    (c) ⬚ is 1000 more than 89,800.

    (d) ⬚ is 1000 less than 28,481.

    (e) ⬚ is 1 less than −10.

    (f) ⬚ is 1 more than −20.

5. Which number is represented by each letter?

    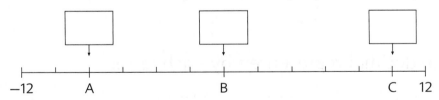

6. Which one of the following is the greatest?

    70,582,   78,502,   75,802,   78,205

    _____

7. Which one of the following is the smallest?

    (a) 3, 0.3, 0.03, 30 _____

    (b) −3, 0, 3, 10, −10 _____

8. There were about 24,500 spectators at a football game. For which of the following is the estimate most accurate?

    24,561, 24,391, 24,519, 24,083 _____

9. Write down the first two common multiples of 6 and 5.

    _____

10. Find the value of the following expressions.

    (a) $100 - 75 + 48 \div 3$ (b) $40 + 13 \times (12 + 6)$

    (c) $1475 - (18 \times 21)$ (d) $900 - (600 - 143)$

11. Which one of the following is equal to $\frac{2}{3}$?
    $\frac{8}{12}$, $\frac{6}{12}$, $\frac{3}{12}$, $\frac{2}{6}$

    _____

12. Which is greater, $\frac{3}{8}$ or $\frac{7}{12}$?

    _____

13. How many sixths are there in $2\frac{1}{6}$?

    _____

14. Express $3\frac{2}{5}$ as a decimal.

    _____

15. Write the decimal represented by each letter.

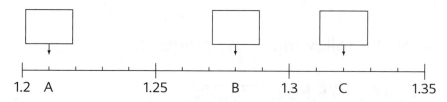

16. Complete the regular number pattern.

   3.5,   4,   _____,   _____,   5.5

17. Brandy bought 3 yd of raffia. She used $\frac{5}{6}$ yd to make
   a doll. Find the length of the raffia left.   _____

18. After selling $\frac{1}{2}$ of his apples, Carlos had 15 apples left.
   How many apples did he have at first?   _____

19. John made 15 flower pot hangers. He used $\frac{2}{3}$ m of wire
   for each hanger. Find the length of wire he used
   altogether.   _____

20. Ben had $35. He spent $\frac{2}{7}$ of it on a pair of shoes.
   How much money did he have left?   _____

21. The figure shows a circle inside a square.

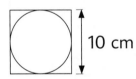

   (a) What is the diameter of the circle?   _____

   (b) What is the radius of the circle?   _____

   (c) What is the perimeter of the square?   _____

   (d) What is the area of the square?   _____

   (e) What are the three types of quadrilaterals
       the following figure can be classified as? _____

                                                  _____

                                                  _____

22. Measure the marked angle.

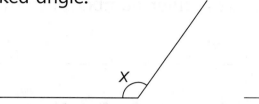

_____

23. Which one of the marked angles in the figure is greater than 2 right angles?

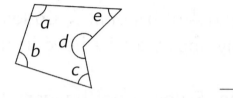

_____

24. 1650 students took part in a parade. There were twice as many boys as girls. How many boys were there in the parade?

_____

25. Mrs. Rowley bought a refrigerator. She paid a down payment of $160 and 8 monthly instalments of $95 each. How much did she pay altogether?

26. There are 36 students in a class. $\frac{2}{3}$ of them are girls. $\frac{1}{4}$ of the girls wear glasses. How many girls wear glasses?

---

27. The rectangle has the same perimeter as the square. Find the length of each side of the square.

13 cm

19 cm

EXERCISE 1

1. Add.

(a)

(0.1) (0.1) (0.1)　　　　(0.1) (0.1) (0.1) (0.1) (0.1)

$0.3 + 0.5 =$

(b)

(0.1) (0.1) (0.1) (0.1) (0.1)　　(0.1) (0.1) (0.1) (0.1)
(0.1) (0.1) (0.1)

$0.8 + 0.4 =$

(c) $0.2 + 0.4 =$

(d) $0.9 + 0.1 =$

(e) $0.5 + 0.9 =$

2. Add.

(a)

(0.01) (0.01) (0.01) (0.01)　　　(0.01) (0.01)

$0.04 + 0.02 =$

(b)

(0.01) (0.01) (0.01) (0.01) (0.01)　　(0.01) (0.01) (0.01) (0.01) (0.01)
(0.01) (0.01)

$0.07 + 0.05 =$

(c) $0.03 + 0.02 =$

(d) $0.09 + 0.01 =$

(e) $0.07 + 0.04 =$

EXERCISE 2

1. Add.

(a)

| 1 | 1 | | 0.1 | 0.1 | 0.1 | 0.1 | 0.1 |

0.1 0.1 0.1 0.1 0.1

0.1

2.6 + 0.5 =

(b)
1 1   1 1 1

0.1 0.1 0.1 0.1

2.4 + 3 =

(c) 4.5 + 6 =

(d) 5.4 + 0.8 =

2. Add.

(a) 3.2 + 1.8 =	(b) 4.6 + 3.7 =
$\quad\quad 3\,.\,2$ $+\quad 1\,.\,8$ $\overline{}$	
(c) 5.9 + 7.8	(d) 8.4 + 7.9 =

EXERCISE 3

1. Add.

(a)

2.53 + 0.2 =

(b)

2.53 + 0.02 =

(c)

4.65 + 0.4 =

(d)

3.87 + 0.7 =

(e)

5.34 + 0.9 =

(f)

3.82 + 0.06 =

(g)

2.63 + 0.07 =

(h)

4.29 + 0.05 =

2. Add.

(a) 0.65 + 0.27 = $\ \ 0.65$ $\underline{+\ \ \ 0.27}$	(b) 0.64 + 2.39 =
(c) 1.8 + 0.56 =	(d) 24.48 + 3.8 =
(e) 1.43 + 2.19 =	(f) 8.25 + 1.36 =
(g) 12.84 + 4.5 =	(h) 46.75 + 21.43 =

EXERCISE 4

1. For each of the following, estimate the value. Then add.

15 + 30 =			
$\begin{array}{r} 14.74 \\ +\ 28.16 \\ \hline \end{array}$	$\begin{array}{r} 8.65 \\ +\ 11.86 \\ \hline \end{array}$	$\begin{array}{r} 41.8 \\ +\ 2.29 \\ \hline \end{array}$	$\begin{array}{r} 66.19 \\ +\ 23.81 \\ \hline \end{array}$
A	L	H	C
$\begin{array}{r} 5.06 \\ +\ 6.3 \\ \hline \end{array}$	$\begin{array}{r} 27.8 \\ +\ 39.1 \\ \hline \end{array}$	$\begin{array}{r} 21 \\ +\ 12.6 \\ \hline \end{array}$	$\begin{array}{r} 54.45 \\ +\ 8.55 \\ \hline \end{array}$
A	E	W	I
$\begin{array}{r} 24.81 \\ +\ 2.54 \\ \hline \end{array}$	$\begin{array}{r} 31.4 \\ +\ 57.35 \\ \hline \end{array}$	$\begin{array}{r} 60 \\ +\ 8.05 \\ \hline \end{array}$	$\begin{array}{r} 77.99 \\ +\ 4.01 \\ \hline \end{array}$
T	N	R	G

Write the letters which match the answers.
You will find the world's longest man-made structure.

82	68.05	66.9	42.9	27.35		33.6	42.9	20.51	20.51

OF

90	44.09	63	88.75	11.36

EXERCISE 5

1. Subtract.

(a)

$$\textcircled{0.1}\,\textcircled{0.1}\,\textcircled{0.1}\,\textcircled{0.1}\,\textcircled{0.1}\,\textcircled{0.1}\,\cancel{\textcircled{0.1}}\,\cancel{\textcircled{0.1}}\,\cancel{\textcircled{0.1}}\,\cancel{\textcircled{0.1}}$$

$$1 - 0.4 =$$

(b)

$$\textcircled{0.1}\,\textcircled{0.1}\,\textcircled{0.1}\,\textcircled{0.1}\,\textcircled{0.1}\qquad\textcircled{0.1}\,\textcircled{0.1}\,\textcircled{0.1}\,\textcircled{0.1}$$
$$\cancel{\textcircled{0.1}}\,\cancel{\textcircled{0.1}}\,\cancel{\textcircled{0.1}}\,\cancel{\textcircled{0.1}}\,\cancel{\textcircled{0.1}}$$

$$1.4 - 0.5 =$$

(c)

$$1.2 - 0.9 =$$

(d)

$$4.3 - 0.4 =$$

2. Subtract.

(a) $5.7 - 0.4 =$

$$\begin{array}{r} 5.7 \\ -\ 0.4 \\ \hline \end{array}$$

(b) $3.1 - 0.5 =$

(c) $4.06 - 0.9 =$

(d) $3 - 0.8 =$

EXERCISE 6

1. Subtract.

    (a)

    $0.08 - 0.03 =$

    (b)
    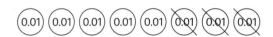

    $1 - 0.35 =$

    (c)
    $0.9 - 0.05 =$

    (d)
    $1 - 0.08 =$

2. Subtract.

    (a)

    $4.41 - 0.03 =$

    (b)

    $1.5 - 0.02 =$

3. Subtract.

(a) 0.48 − 0.06 = $\begin{array}{r} 0.48 \\ -\ 0.06 \\ \hline \end{array}$	(b) 3.27 − 0.03 =
(c) 2.83 − 0.05 =	(d) 6.15 − 0.09 =
(e) 2.7 − 0.08 =	(f) 4.3 − 0.07 =
(g) 5.1 − 0.06 =	(h) 4 − 0.09 =

EXERCISE 7

1. Subtract.

(a) 3.7 − 1.6 = 3.7 -1.6 $\overline{}$	(b) 5.6 − 2.9 =
(c) 7.4 − 3.8 =	(d) 4.3 − 2.7 =
(e) 4 − 1.8 =	(f) 7 − 5.6 =
(g) 8 − 3.9 =	(h) 6 − 2.4 =

EXERCISE 8

1. Subtract.

(a) 8.74 − 6.3 = $$\begin{array}{r} 8.74 \\ -\ 6.30 \\ \hline \end{array}$$	(b) 6.45 − 3.9 =
(c) 0.6 − 0.53 =	(d) 9.5 − 0.72 =
(e) 4.86 − 1.62 =	(f) 8.41 − 3.65 =
(g) 7 − 0.85 =	(h) 10 − 4.57 =

2. Subtract.

4.91 − 2.56	8 − 4.92	0.9 − 0.47	12.05 − 7.4
T	**E**	**H**	**U**
9.4 − 4.73	1.38 − 0.6	16.42 − 9.18	3 − 1.63
R	**P**	**C**	**S**
11.76 − 4.38	10.06 − 5.9	15 − 6.04	10.6 − 3.82
I	**G**	**O**	**N**

What birds cannot fly?

Write the letters which match the answers.
You will find two of them.

0.78	3.08	6.78	4.16	4.65	7.38	6.78

8.96	1.37	2.35	4.67	7.38	7.24	0.43

EXERCISE 9

1. Write the missing numbers.

   (a) $5.24 \xrightarrow{\;+2\;}$ ☐ $\xrightarrow{\;-0.01\;}$ ☐

   $5.24 + 1.99 =$ ☐

   (b) $7.63 \xrightarrow{\;+4\;}$ ☐ $\xrightarrow{\;-0.05\;}$ ☐

   $7.63 + 3.95 =$ ☐

   (c) $4.82 \xrightarrow{\;-3\;}$ ☐ $\xrightarrow{\;+0.01\;}$ ☐

   $4.82 - 2.99 =$ ☐

   (d) $6.05 \xrightarrow{\;-2\;}$ ☐ $\xrightarrow{\;+0.02\;}$ ☐

   $6.05 - 1.98 =$ ☐

2. For each of the following, estimate the value. Then add.

(a) $6.81 + 2.98 =$	$7 + 3 =$
(b) $8.69 + 1.95 =$	

3. For each of the following, estimate the value. Then subtract.

(a) $8.25 - 3.99 =$	
(b) $7.53 - 2.95 =$	

EXERCISE 10

1. Mitchell had a wire 5 yd long. After using a length of it, he had 2.35 yd of the wire left. How much wire did he use?

    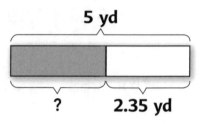

    5 yd

    ?   2.35 yd

2. A baby boy weighed 3.6 kg at birth. After a month, he weighed 5 kg. How much weight did he gain?

    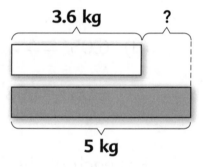

    3.6 kg   ?

    5 kg

3. Mr. Smith brought $36.45 to a mall.
    He came home with $2.54.
    How much did he spend at the mall?

    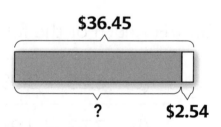

    $36.45

    ? $2.54

4. Sally had $13.50. She spent $1.40 on bus fare and $2.50 on lunch. How much did she have left?

5. Betty bought a vase for $12 and a bunch of flowers for $4.50. She gave the salesgirl $20. How much change did she receive?

6. Mrs. Lee bought an iron and a kettle. The iron cost $38.90. The kettle cost $6.50 more than the iron. How much did she spend altogether?

---

7. Ribbon A is 0.38 ft longer than Ribbon B. Ribbon A is 0.25 ft shorter than Ribbon C. If Ribbon C is 1.63 ft long, find the length of Ribbon B.

EXERCISE 11

1. Multiply.

(a)

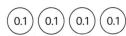

   $0.4 \times 2 =$

(b)

   $0.6 \times 3 =$

(c)

   $0.2 \times 7 =$

(d)

   $0.9 \times 4 =$

(e)

   $0.5 \times 6 =$

(f)

   $0.7 \times 8 =$

(g)

   $0.3 \times 9 =$

(h)

   $0.8 \times 5 =$

2. Multiply.

(a)

$0.03 \times 2 =$

(b)

$0.07 \times 4 =$

(c)

$0.02 \times 9 =$

(d)

$0.05 \times 7 =$

(e)

$0.06 \times 5 =$

(f)

$0.09 \times 8 =$

(g)

$0.04 \times 3 =$

(h)

$0.08 \times 6 =$

EXERCISE 12

1. Multiply.

(a) 4.3 × 2 = $$\begin{array}{r} 4.3 \\ \times \quad 2 \\ \hline \end{array}$$	(b) 6.4 × 3 =
(c) 2.8 × 6 =	(d) 4.7 × 9 =

2. For each of the following, estimate the product.
    Then multiply.

(a) 6.9 × 4 =	7 × 4 =	(b) 7 × 5.5 =	
(c) 26.5 × 5 =		(d) 8 × 30.6 =	

EXERCISE 13

1. Multiply.

(a) 0.83 × 2 = $\begin{array}{r} 0.83 \\ \times 2 \\ \hline \end{array}$	(b) 0.12 × 6 =
(c) 5.26 × 3 =	(d) 6.75 × 4 =

2. For each of the following, estimate the product.
   Then multiply.

(a) 7.03 × 6 =	7 × 6 =	(b) 8 × 5.64 =	
(c) 82.78 × 7		(d) 9 × 64.72 =	

3. Multiply.

0.48 × 2	20.3 × 4	0.03 × 7	4.91 × 3
L	**H**	**E**	**Y**
6.45 × 5	93.5 × 6	80.7 × 9	7.16 × 9
T	**E**	**P**	**E**
12.15 × 3	408.2 × 8	14.47 × 2	13.08 × 6
N	**D**	**H**	**E**

Write the letters which match the answers.
You will find a message.

81.2	561	0.96	726.3		32.25	28.94	0.21

36.45	64.44	78.48	3265.6	14.73

EXERCISE 14

1. Lynn bought 3 pieces of ribbon each 1.25 yd long. Find the total length of the ribbons.

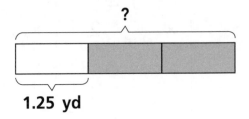

2. A bucket can hold 5.7 liters of water. A fish tank can hold 5 times as much water as the bucket. Find the capacity of the fish tank.

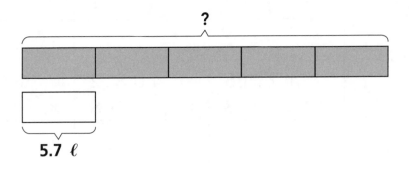

3. Cameron saved $2.50 a week for 6 weeks. How much did he save altogether?

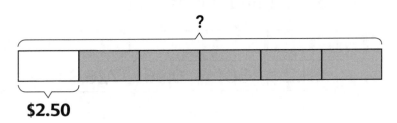

Unit 7: The Four Operations of Decimals

4. Complete the following bills.

Chocolate	Crackers	1 can of chocolate $_____
1 can for $6.90	1 pack for $1.45	2 packs of crackers $_____
		Total $_____
Nuts	Sauce	2 bags of nuts $_____
1 bag for $3.75	1 bottle for 95¢	2 bottles of sauce $_____
		Total $_____
Bath towels	Face towels	1 bath towel $_____
$9.95 each	$1.20 each	4 face towels $_____
		Total $_____
Teddy bear	Dolls	3 dolls $_____
$16.50	$8 each	1 teddy bear $_____
		Total $_____

5. Sharon bought a piece of material 5 m long. She made 2 pillowcases with it. If she used 0.85 m of material for each pillow case, how much material did she have left?

6. Mimi spent $1.35 a day for 6 days. She had $2.50 left. How much money did she have at first?

EXERCISE 15

1. Divide.

(a)

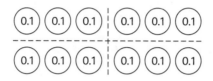

$0.8 \div 2 =$

(b)

$1.2 \div 4 =$

(c)

$0.9 \div 3 =$

(d)

$2.4 \div 6 =$

(e)

$2.8 \div 7 =$

(f)

$3 \div 5 =$

(g)

$\$6.30 \div 9 =$

(h)

$\$4.20 \div 7 =$

2. Divide.

(a)

$0.12 \div 2 =$

(b)

$0.15 \div 3 =$

(c) $0.08 \div 2 =$

(d) $0.24 \div 4 =$

(e) $0.3 \div 5 =$

(f) $0.42 \div 7 =$

(g) $\$0.54 \div 6 =$

(h) $\$0.40 \div 8 =$

Unit 7: The Four Operations of Decimals

EXERCISE 16

1. Divide.

(a) $0.48 \div 2 =$ $2\overline{)0.48}$	(b) $0.63 \div 3 =$
(c) $0.65 \div 5 =$	(d) $0.95 \div 5 =$
(e) $0.84 \div 3 =$	(f) $0.76 \div 4 =$
(g) $0.78 \div 6 =$	(h) $0.96 \div 8 =$

EXERCISE 17

1. Divide.

(a) $8.26 \div 2 =$ $2 \overline{)8.26}$	(b) $9.66 \div 3 =$
(c) $7.35 \div 5 =$	(d) $5.36 \div 2 =$
(e) $68.25 \div 3 =$	(f) $42.16 \div 8 =$
(g) $80.56 \div 4 =$	(h) $35.25 \div 5 =$

2. Divide.

(a) $4\overline{)\$4.20}$	(b) $8\overline{)\$9.20}$
(c) $5\overline{)\$7.25}$	(d) $7\overline{)\$9.45}$
(e) $6\overline{)\$6.90}$	(f) $5\overline{)\$5.45}$
(g) $3\overline{)\$7.65}$	(h) $9\overline{)\$15.75}$

3. Divide.

(a) $2\overline{)9.7}$	(b) $4\overline{)60.6}$
(c) $8\overline{)94}$	(d) $5\overline{)48.6}$
(e) $4\overline{)150}$	(f) $8\overline{)26}$
(g) $8\overline{)2}$	(h) $6\overline{)176.1}$

EXERCISE 18

1. Divide.

(a) $7 \div 5 =$ $5\overline{)7}$	(b) $6 \div 8 =$
(c) $0.5 \div 2 =$	(d) $3.8 \div 4 =$
(e) $6.2 \div 5 =$	(f) $7.5 \div 6 =$
(g) $33 \div 4 =$	(h) $46.8 \div 8 =$

2. Find the unit cost of each item below.

(a) 8 towels cost $7.60.

1 towel costs _____.

(b) 4 notebooks cost $3.40.

1 notebook costs _____.

(c) 3 erasers cost $1.05.

1 eraser costs _____.

(d) 7 pears cost $7.35.

1 pear costs _____.

EXERCISE 19

1. For each of the following, estimate the quotient. Then divide. Give each answer correct to 1 decimal place.

35 ÷ 7 =			
7⟌32.4	3⟌61	3⟌22.74	5⟌30.2
6⟌32.94	9⟌28.9	4⟌37	8⟌17.28

Color the spaces which contain the answers.
What number does it show?

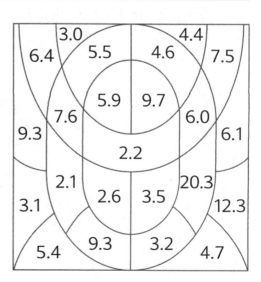

The number is _____.

EXERCISE 20

1. Jane cuts a rope 1.48 m long into 4 equal pieces. Find the length of each piece.

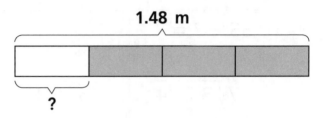

2. Mrs. Gray paid $20.40 for 3 kg of shrimp. Find the cost of 1 kg of shrimp.

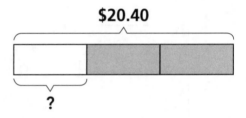

3. Danielle spent $28.25 at a bookshop. She spent 5 times as much as Holly. How much did Holly spend?

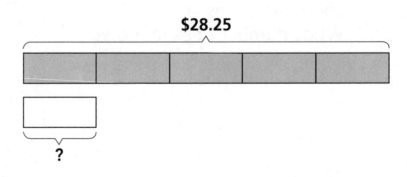

4. Gwen and Susan bought the box of crackers and the tub of ice cream. They shared the cost equally. How much did each girl pay?

Crackers $3.15

Ice cream $4.65

5. Angela bought 5 kg of grapes. She gave the cashier $50 and received $18.75 change. Find the cost of 1 kg of grapes.

6. The total weight of 5 blocks of butter and a bag of flour is 2.7 lb. If the weight of the bag of flour is 1.2 lb, find the weight of each block of butter.

7. A painter mixed 10.5 liters of white paint with 15.5 liters of red paint. He poured the mixture equally into 4 cans. How much paint was there in each can?

REVIEW 7

1. What is the greatest 5-digit number that can be formed using all of the digits 0, 1, 9, 5 and 8? _____

2. What does each of the digits in 9,638,300 stand for?

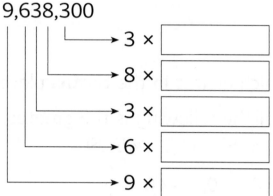

9,638,300

- 3 × [   ]
- 8 × [   ]
- 3 × [   ]
- 6 × [   ]
- 9 × [   ]

3. The value of the digit **6** in 32.**6**4 is _____.

4. In 30.49, which digit is in the hundredths place? _____

5. Write the missing number in each of the following regular number patterns.

   (a) 50,230, _____, 46,230, 44,230

   (b) 71.54, 71.04, _____, 70.04

6. Quadrilateral ABCD is a parallelogram.

If AB // CD, then BC // _____.

7. How much is $\frac{2}{5}$ of $10? _____

8. Express 1100 g as a fraction of 2 kg. _____

9. Write each fraction as a decimal.

   (a) $5\frac{1}{4}$ _____

   (b) $16\frac{4}{5}$ _____

10. Write each decimal as a fraction in its simplest form.

    (a) 0.85 _____

    (b) 2.4 _____

11. In 23.56, which digit is in the **tenths** place? _____

12. Which one of the following is the greatest?

    (a) 49.05, 495, 4.95, 45.09 _____

    (b) −20, 30, 10, −40 _____

13. Round 6.29 to 1 decimal place. _____

14. Round $35.05 to the nearest dollar. _____

15. Write the answer for each of the following as a decimal or whole number.

    (a) 4 tenths + 9 tenths = _____

    (b) 7 tenths + 3 tenths = _____

    (c) 4 hundredths + 6 hundredths = _____

    (d) 12 tenths − 9 tenths = _____

    (e) 9 tenths 10 hundredths − 8 hundredths = _____

    (f) 20 hundredths × 8 = _____

    (g) 72 hundredths ÷ 9 = _____

16. Divide. Give the answer correct to 1 decimal place.

    (a) 123.6 ÷ 7 _____

    (b) 307 ÷ 4 _____

17. What is the missing number in each [   ] ?

   (a) [   ] is 0.01 more than 6.04.

   (b) [   ] is 0.1 less than 3.8.

   (c) 5.61 = 5 + [   ]

   (d) 16.7 = 10 + [   ]

18. Fill in each ( ) with >, < or =.

   (a) 12.62 ( ) 12.26   (b) 8.70 ( ) 8.7

   (c) −131 ( ) −142

19. Insert parentheses to make the following equations true.

   (a) 12 − 3 × 2 + 9 = 15

   (b) 12 − 3 × 2 + 9 = 99

20. Find the value of each of the following expressions.

   (a) 104.8 + 8.5   _____

   (b) 4.06 − 0.9   _____

   (c) 6.35 − 0.14   _____

   (d) 34.18 × 7   _____

   (e) 22.14 ÷ 6   _____

21. Apples are sold at 3 for $1.56. How many
    apples can Alice buy with $5?   _____

22. David took 3 hours 25 minutes to paint his room.
    He finished painting his room at 1:40 p.m.
    At what time did he start painting his room?   _____

23. The stadium is 4 km 360 m from Nicky's apartment. It is 1 km 250 m from Brian's apartment. How much further is the stadium from Nicky's apartment than from Brian's apartment? _____

Stadium   Brian's apartment   Nicky's apartment

1 km 250 m

24. Taylor made 98 sugar buns and 42 plain buns. What fraction of the buns were plain buns?

_____

25. Roger spent $\frac{1}{5}$ of his monthly salary on food. He spent twice as much money on transport as on food. What fraction of his monthly salary was spent on transport?

_____

26. The total weight of two bags of flour is 2 lb. One of them weighs $\frac{1}{4}$ lb. What is the weight of the other bag of flour? _____

27. Joe had $24. He used $\frac{3}{8}$ of it to buy a book. What was the cost of the book? _____

28. One side of a parallelogram is 8.5 cm and another side is 4.8 cm. What is the perimeter of the parallelogram? _____

29. The length of a rectangle is twice its width. Find the length of the rectangle if its perimeter is 95.4 m.

_____

30. A rectangular garden measures 35 m by 24 m. What is the cost of putting up a fence around the garden if 1 m of fencing costs $10? _____

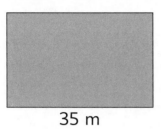

24 m

35 m

31. The area of a rectangular vegetable plot is 35 yd². If the length of the vegetable plot is 7 yd, find its width.

_____

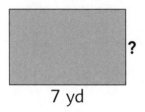

?

7 yd

32. In the figure, ∠XYZ is 46°. Measure ∠WYZ. _____

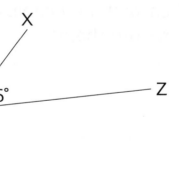

33.

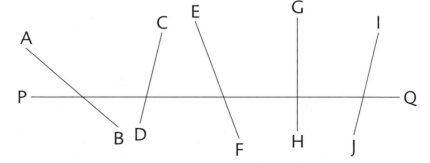

(a) Name a pair of parallel lines. _____

(b) Name a pair of perpendicular lines. _____

34. The perimeter of a rectangle is 48 in. The length of the rectangle is twice its width. Find the length of the rectangle.

_____

35. There are 84 children in a choir. $\frac{5}{6}$ of them are girls. How many boys are there?

EXERCISE 1

1. Look at the shapes
    Name the pairs that are congruent.

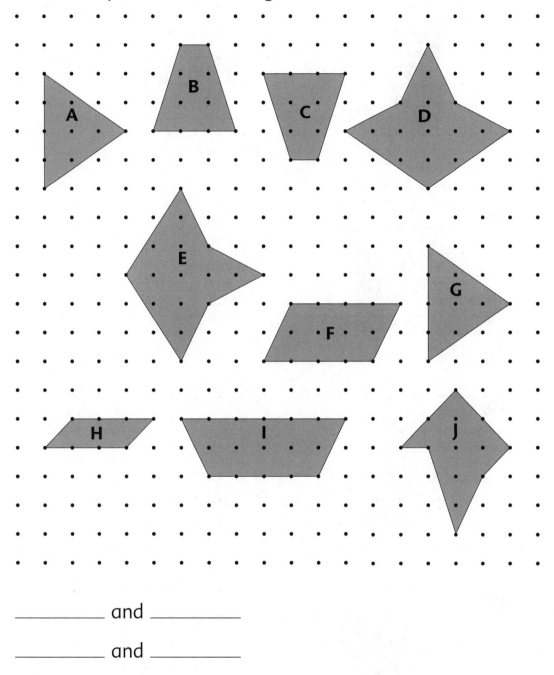

_____ and _____

_____ and _____

_____ and _____

2. Draw a figure congruent to the given one but in a new position.

Example:

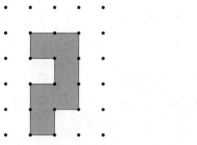 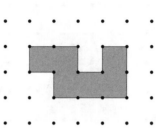

(a)

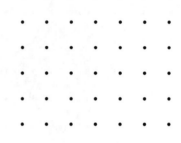

(b)

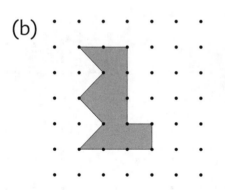

(c)

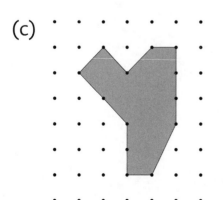

Unit 8: Congruent and Symmetric Figures

3. ABCDE is congruent to FGHIJ.

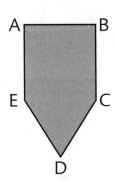 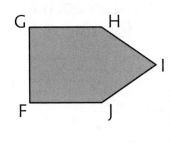

(a) Vertex A corresponds to Vertex _____.

(b) Side BC corresponds to Side _____.

(c) Side HI corresponds to Side _____.

(d) Vertex G corresponds to Vertex _____.

(e) Side DE corresponds to Side _____.

EXERCISE 2

1. Color the shape used in each of the following tessellations. (a) has been done for you.

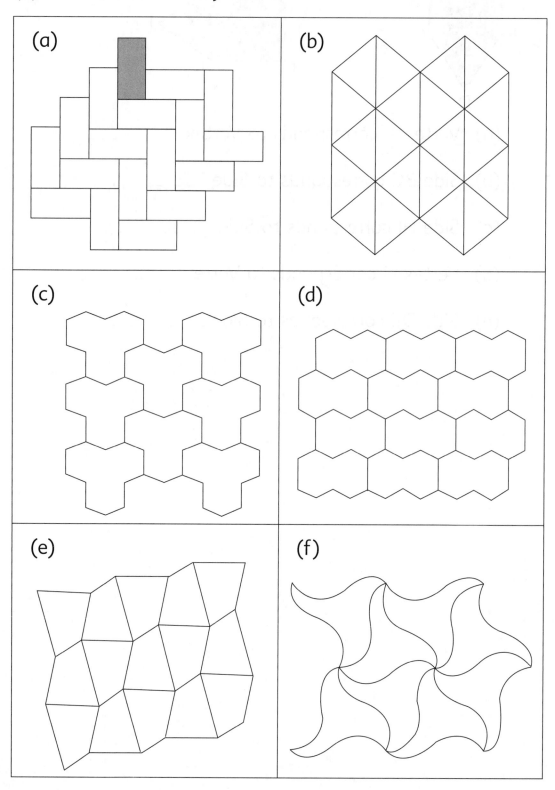

Unit 8: Congruent and Symmetric Figures

2. Extend each of the following tessellations in the space provided.

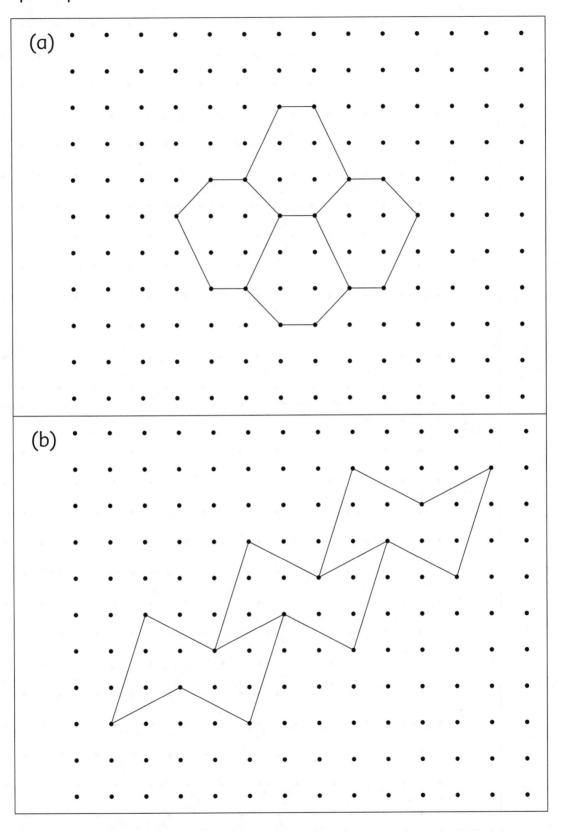

(a)

(b)

(c)

(d)

Unit 8: Congruent and Symmetric Figures

EXERCISE 3

1.   Does each of the following shapes tessellate?
     Write **Yes** or **No** in the given box.

(a)

(b)

(c)

(d)

Unit 8: Congruent and Symmetric Figures

EXERCISE 4

1. In each of the following, use the given shape to make a tessellation in the space provided.

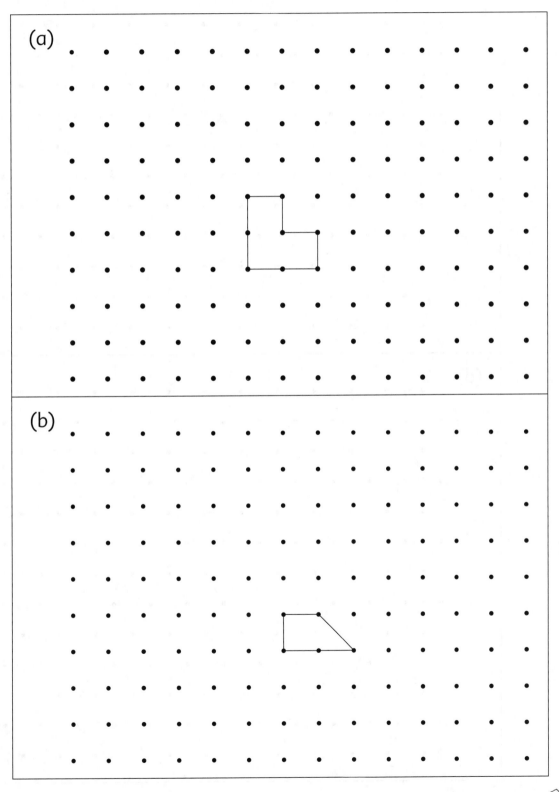

(a)

(b)

(c)

(d)

Unit 8: Congruent and Symmetric Figures

2. Use the given shape to make two different tessellations in the spaces provided.

   (a) Tessellation 1

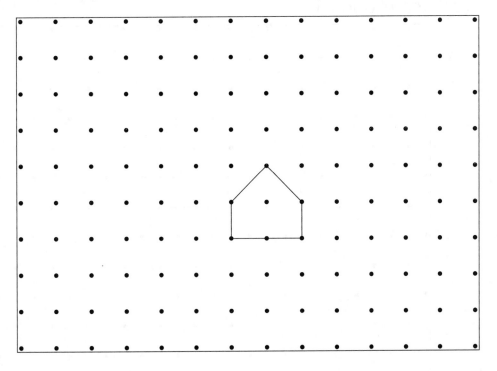

   (b) Tessellation 2

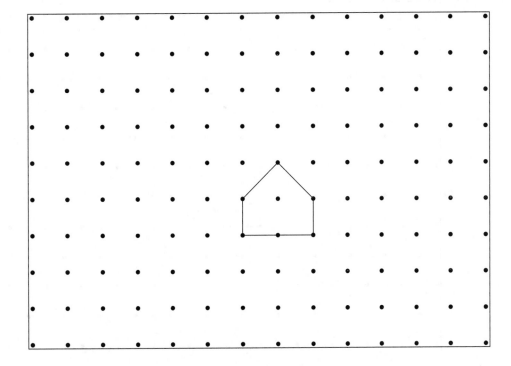

3. Use the given shape to make two different tessellations in the spaces provided.

   (a) Tessellation 1

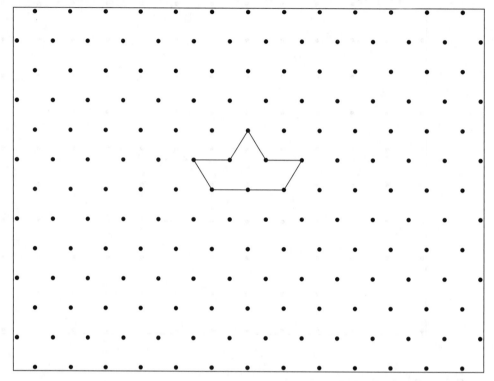

   (b) Tessellation 2

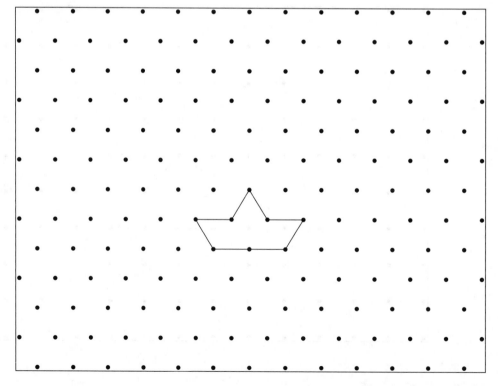

Unit 8: Congruent and Symmetric Figures

EXERCISE 5

1. Fold a piece of paper.
   Cut out a figure and then unfold it.
   You will get a symmetric figure.

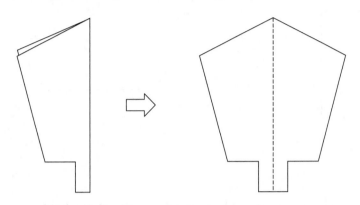

Complete the following symmetric figures.

(a)

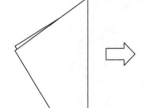

(b)

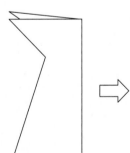

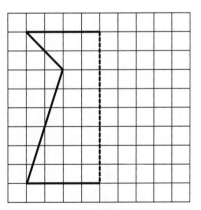

2. A symmetric figure can be cut out from a piece of paper like this:

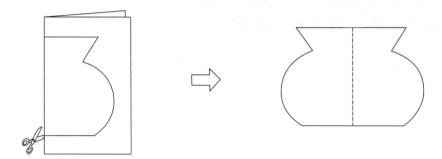

Match each of these with the correct symmetric figures below.

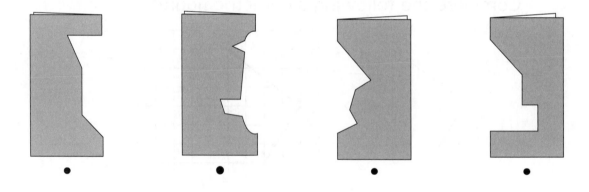

Unit 8: Congruent and Symmetric Figures

EXERCISE 6

1. Some of the following figures are symmetric figures.
   Draw a line of symmetry in each symmetric figure.

(a)
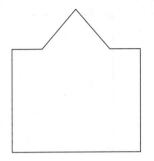

(b)
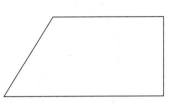

(c)
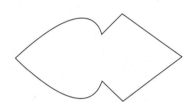

(d)
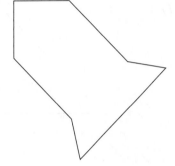

(e)

(f)
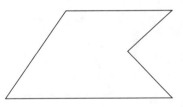

(g)
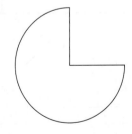

(h)
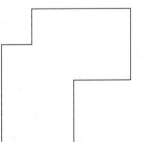

2. In each of the following figures, is the dotted line a line of symmetry? Write **Yes** or **No**.

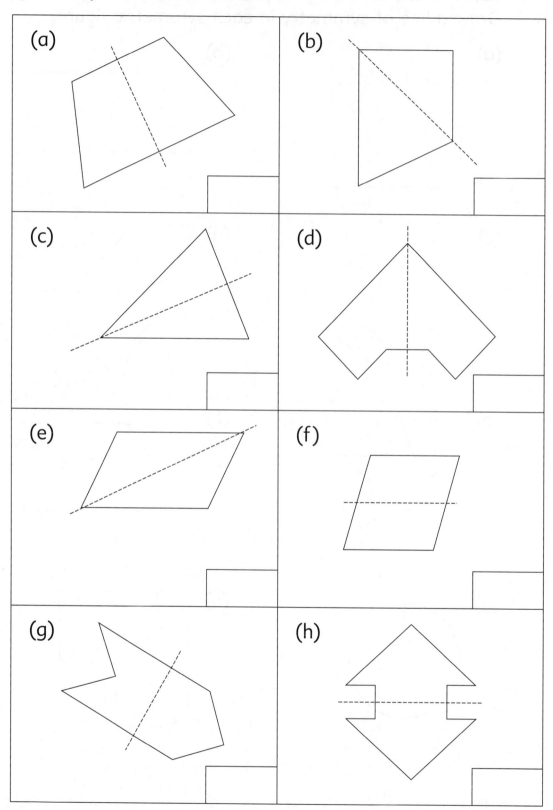

(a)

(b)

(c)

(d)

(e)

(f)

(g)

(h)

EXERCISE 7

1. Each of the following shows half of a letter.
    Draw the other half of each letter.
    (The dotted line is a line of symmetry.)

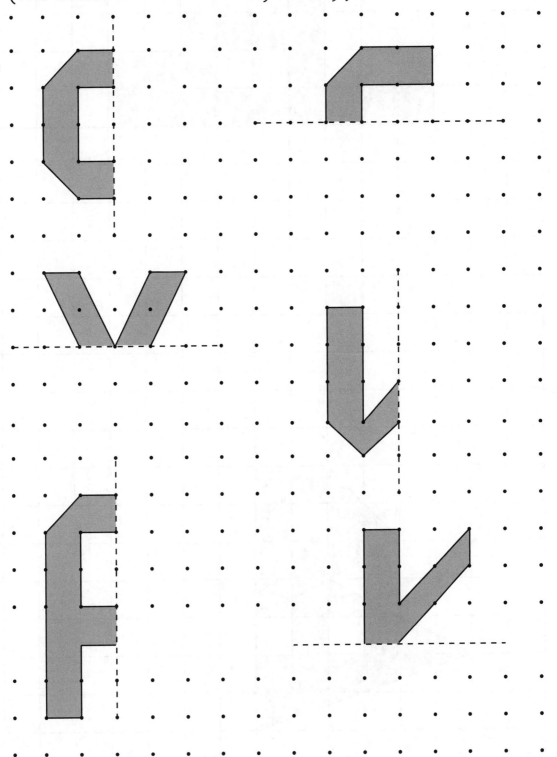

2. Use the dotted line as a line of symmetry.
   Complete the following symmetric figures.

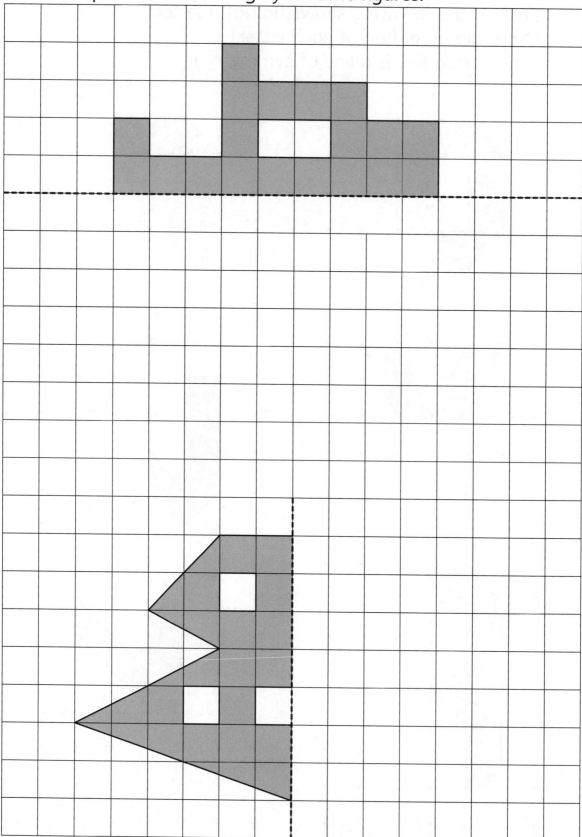

EXERCISE 8

1. Look at the pictures.
    Check (✓) the correct column.

	Line symmetry	Rotational symmetry

2. Draw some figures that have rotational symmetry.

REVIEW 8

1. Arrange the numbers in decreasing order.

   (a) 10,050, 9950, 9590, 10,590, 9190

   _____

   (b) 8.3, 2.83, 2.05, 7.28

   _____

   (c) −20, −34, 62, 21, −42

   _____

2. Find the value of each of the following.

   (a) 54.86 + 2.9   _____

   (b) 10.5 − 6.07   _____

   (c) 60.45 ÷ 3   _____

   (d) 35.25 × 8   _____

3. Use parentheses to make the following equations true.
   (a) 24 ÷ 6 ÷ 2 + 3 = 5

   _____

   (b) 24 ÷ 6 ÷ 2 + 3 = 11

   _____

4. (a) Round the sum of 38.59 and 12.62 to
       1 decimal place.   _____

   (b) Round the product of 4.85 and 9 to the
       nearest whole number.   _____

5. Express $2\frac{3}{5}$ as an improper fraction. _____

6. Express $\frac{19}{4}$ as a mixed number. _____

7. Express 4.24 as a fraction in the simplest form. _____

8. Express $6\frac{4}{5}$ as a decimal. _____

9. What number is 0.7 more than 25.38? _____

10. Write the decimal represented by each letter.

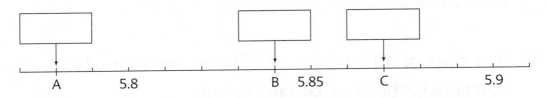

11. Write the missing decimal in each of the following.
    (a) 32.82 = 6.45 + _____
    (b) 56.04 − _____ = 21.99
    (c) 8 × _____ = 17.12
    (d) _____ ÷ 6 = 41.1

12. Jim left his home at 8:15 a.m. He returned at 5:50 p.m.
    How long was he away from home? _____

13. John is 1.7 m tall. His brother is 0.46 m shorter than he.
    How tall is his brother? _____

14. Miss Rowley made 4 jars of butter biscuits and 6 jars of
    jam biscuits. There were 48 biscuits in each jar.
    How many biscuits did she make altogether? _____

15. Violet cut a pizza into 8 equal pieces. She gave 2 pieces of the pizza to her neighbor. What fraction of the pizza did she have left? (Give the answer in its simplest form.) _____

16. Chris sleeps 8 hours a day. What fraction of a day does he sleep? _____

17. The capacity of a container is 4 gal. It contains $\frac{3}{5}$ gal of water. How much more water is needed to fill the container? _____

18. In a class of 40 students, $\frac{5}{8}$ of them can swim. How many students in the class **cannot** swim? _____

19. (a) In the figure, ABCD is a rectangle and $\angle DAC = 57°$. Measure $\angle CAB$.

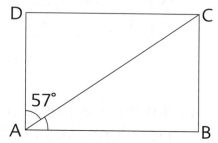

   (b) In the figure, PQR is a straight line and $\angle SQR = 136°$. Measure $\angle PQS$.

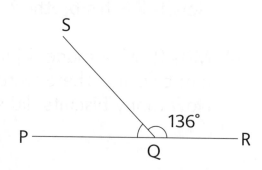

20. A can of beans costs $1.20. A can of peaches costs twice as much. What is the total cost of 1 can of beans and 2 cans of peaches?

21. Put a check (✓) in the table if the figure has line symmetry or rotational symmetry.

	Line symmetry	Rotational symmetry
Square		
Rectangle		
Parallelogram		
Rhombus		
Trapezoid		
Equilateral triangle		
Isosceles triangle		
Scalene triangle		

22. Use the given shape to make two different tessellations in the spaces provided.

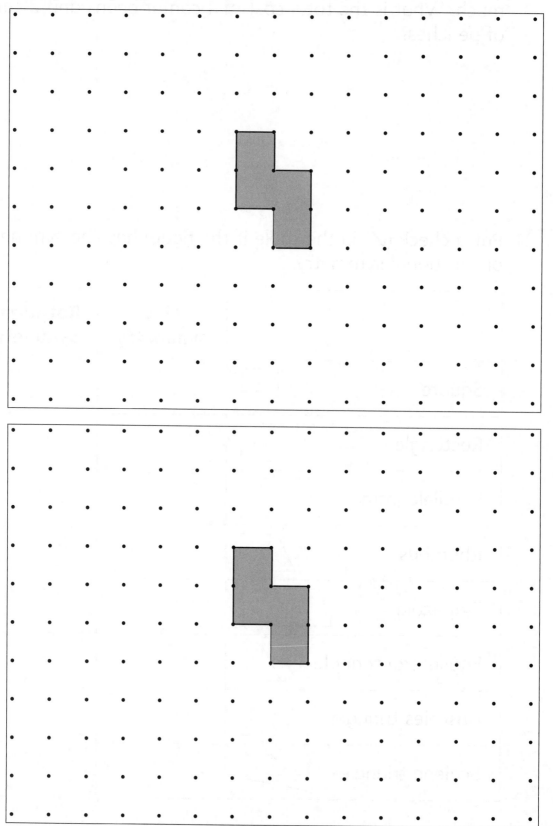

EXERCISE 1

1.

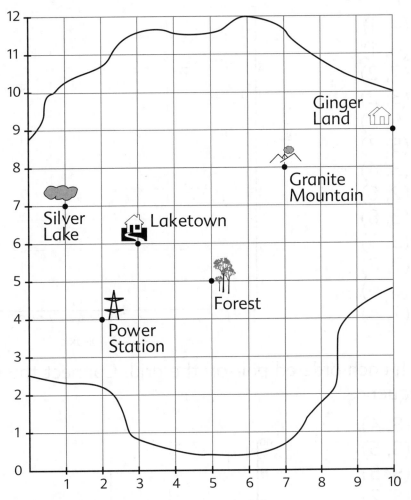

(a) Is Laketown at (6, 3) or at (3, 6)?

(b) Write the ordered pairs of each place listed below.

Place	Coordinates
Granite Mountain	
Silver Lake	
Forest	
Power Station	

(c) A church is located at coordinates (5, 8).
On the map, mark out the location of the church.

(d) Draw a river that starts at (7, 8) and ends at (6, 12).

2. Graph each ordered pair on the grid. Connect the points in sequence.

1. (4, 1)
2. (6, 1)
3. (7, 2)
4. (3, 2)
5. (5, 2)
6. (5, 3)
7. (3, 4)
8. (2, 6)
9. (3, 8)
10. (5, 9)
11. (7, 8)
12. (8, 6)
13. (7, 4)

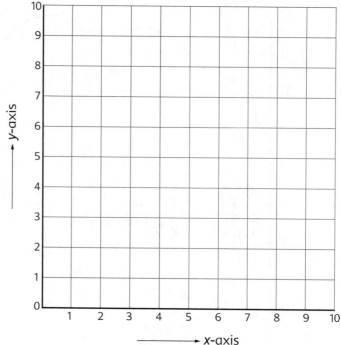

3. Graph each ordered pair on the grid. Connect the points in sequence.

1. (8, 4)
2. (8, 5)
3. (9, 5)
4. (8, 2)
5. (3, 2)
6. (0, 5)
7. (2, 5)
8. (3, 4)
9. (5, 4)
10. (5, 5)
11. (7, 5)
12. (3, 5)
13. (5, 6)
14. (8, 6)
15. (2, 6)
16. (5, 8)
17. (7, 8)
18. (5, 9)

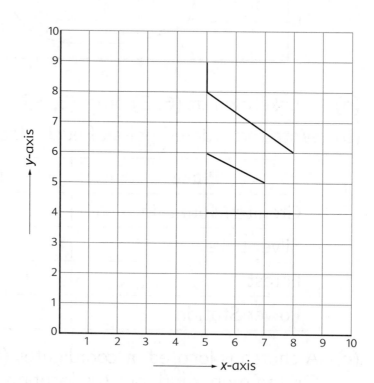

Unit 9: Coordinate Graphs and Changes in Quantities

EXERCISE 2

1. (a) Find the length of each line segment.

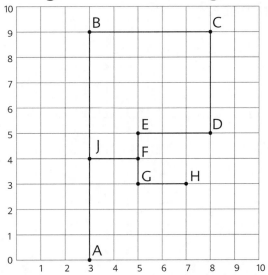

   (i) Line BC = _____ units

   (ii) Line EG = _____ units

   (iii) Line AB = _____ units

   (b) To find the length of DE, do you subtract the first or second coordinates in the ordered pairs for points D and E?

   (c) What is the distance from C to a point at (2, 9)?

2. A rectangle has vertices at (4, 2), (4, 10), (10, 10) and (10, 2). What is its perimeter in units?

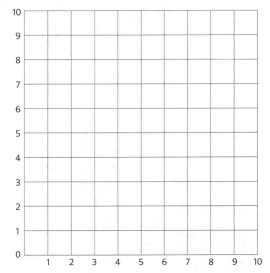

3. A polygon has vertices with the coordinates (4, 4), (4, 7), (6, 7), (6, 8), (3, 8), (3, 10), (8, 10), and (8, 4). What is its perimeter?

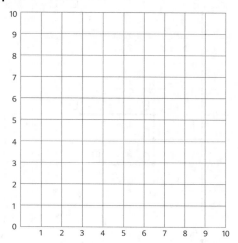

_____ units

4. Point K is at (12, 7). Point P is 10 units from Point K in the vertical direction.
What are the coordinates of Point P?

5. Square A has sides 6 units long.
Vertex A is at point (3, 6).

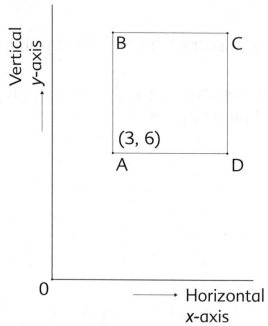

(a) Vertex B is at point _____.

(b) Vertex C is at point _____.

(c) Vertex D is at point _____.

EXERCISE 3

1. Squares, with sides 1 cm, are used to make stairs. How does the perimeter change as the number of steps increases?

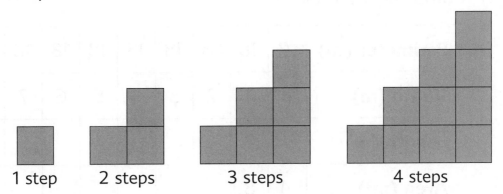

1 step   2 steps   3 steps   4 steps

(a) Complete the table by filling in the perimeters.

Number of steps	1	2	3	4	5	6		n
Perimeter (cm)								

(b) Write a formula for the perimeter, using P to stand for perimeter and n to stand for the number of steps.

$P =$

(c) What is the perimeter if the number of steps is 20?

2. Jake has bought 18 m of fencing. The fencing is in 1-m sections. He wants to find the greatest rectangular area that he can fence with it.

(a) Complete the table.

Perimeter (m)	P	18	18	18	18	18	18	18	18
Width (m)	w	1	2	3	4	5	6	7	8
Length (m)	l	8							
Area (m²)	A	8							

(b) What is the greatest area that he can fence? _____

(c) What is the value of $l + w$? _____

(d) Write an expression showing how the length changes as the width increases by 1 m at a time.

$l =$ _____

3. Complete the table for the equation $m = (99 \times n) + n$.

m	1	2	3	4	5		24
n	0.01			0.04			

EXERCISE 4

1. (a) Complete the table to show how the perimeter (p) of a square changes if the side (s) increases in length by 1 unit each time.

s	1	2	3	4
p				

(b) Write the formula for the perimeter of a square. _____

(c) Graph the relationship between the length and the perimeter.

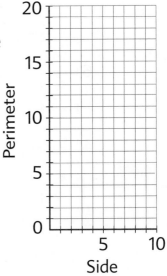

2. (a) Complete the table for the equation $y = 2x + 1$.

x	1	2	3	4	5	6
y						

(b) Graph the values as ordered pairs (x, y).

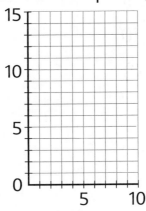

3. (a) Graph the ordered pairs (2, 2), (3, 4), and (4, 6), and connect the points.

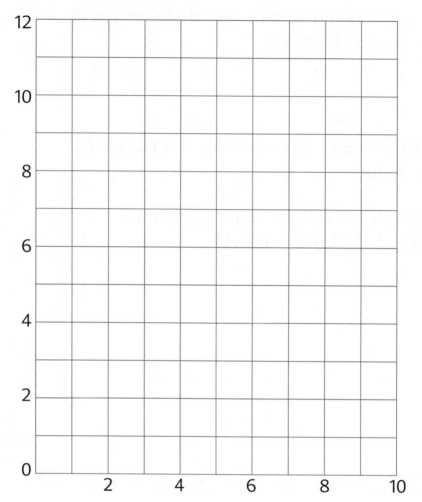

(b) Extend the line. The following points are on the line. Complete the coordinates.

(5, _____)

(_____, 10)

(_____, 0)

REVIEW 9

1. What is the value of the digit **8** in **84,073?** _____

2. Which one of the following is a common factor of 18 and 24?

    4,   6,   8,   12 _____

3. Write the missing number in each of the following.

    (a) 86,049 is [ ] more than 76,049.

    (b) 39,561 is [ ] less than 40,561.

    (c) $7 \times 8 = 8 + 8 +$ [ ] $\times 8$

4. What number is represented by each letter?

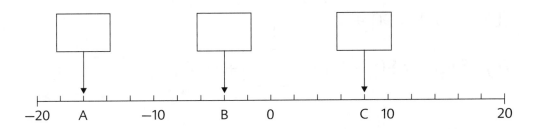

5. Solve each of the following expressions.

    (a) $67 - (100 - 52)$ (b) $(84 - 32) \div 4$

    _____   _____

    (c) $72 \div 6 + 18 \div 3$ (d) $47 - 28 \div 7 \times 8$

    _____   _____

6. Arrange the numbers in increasing order.

   (a) 4.54,   25.4,   20.5,   5.04

   _____

   (b) 10.513,   5.013,   13.015,   3.515

   _____

7. Which one of the following has the digit **6** in the tenths place?

   16.25,   12.**65**,   15.2**6**,   **6**2.15   _____

8. The distance by air between City A and City B is 1444 km. Round this distance to the nearest 100 km.   _____

9. Write the missing number in each of the following.

   (a) 38.56 = 30 + 8 + ☐ + 0.06

   (b) 93.72 = 90 + ☐

   (c) 81.53 = 80 + 1 + ☐ + 0.03

10. $3\frac{1}{4}$ is the same as $\dfrac{\boxed{}}{4}$.

11. Write the fraction represented by each letter.

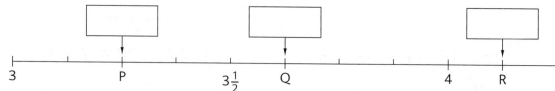

12. Which one of the following fractions is smaller than $\frac{1}{2}$?

    $\dfrac{7}{8}$, $\dfrac{5}{9}$, $\dfrac{2}{5}$, $\dfrac{6}{11}$ _____

13. Arrange the fractions in order, beginning with the greatest.

$1\frac{1}{8}$, $\frac{3}{4}$, $1\frac{4}{5}$, $\frac{5}{6}$

_____

14. What fraction of 1 meter is 20 cm? Write the fraction in its simplest form. _____

15. Jane has 98 stamps. Tyrone has 153 more stamps than Jane. How many stamps do they have altogether? _____

16. There are 14 boxes of pretzels. There are 24 pretzels in each box. How many pretzels are there altogether? _____

17. There are 12 blocks of apartments in a housing project. There are 25 floors in each block of apartments. There are 4 apartments on each floor. How many apartments are there altogether? _____

18. Jack, John and Jim shared the cost of their lunch equally. The lunch cost $49.50. How much did each boy pay? _____

19. Peter jogged 6 times around a circular track of perimeter 0.58 km. How many kilometers did he jog altogether? _____

20. There are 60 workers in a factory. 48 of them are men. What fraction of the workers are women? _____

21. A tank is $\frac{5}{8}$ full. It contains 10 qt of water. What is the capacity of the tank? _____

22. David took 1 hour 35 minutes to travel from his house to the library. He left his house at 9:15 a.m. What time did he arrive at the library? _____

23. How many hours and minutes are there from 10:45 p.m. to 1:30 a.m.? _____

24. Tom bought 10 twenty-cent stamps, 6 thirty-five-cent stamps and 8 fifty-cent stamps. How much did he spend altogether? _____

25. Use the given shape to make a tessellation in the space provided.

26. Does the completed figure have rotational symmetry?

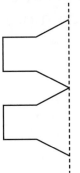

27. A quadrilateral has the coordinates (5, 3), (1, 7), (6, 9) and (10, 5).

(a) Draw the quadrilateral on the grid.
(b) What type of quadrilateral is it? _____

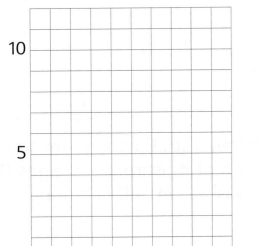

28. A circle with a radius of 4 units has its center at (5, 5).

(a) Fill in the missing number for other points on the circle.

(5, _____), (5, _____),

(_____, 5), (_____, 5)

(b) The diameter of the circle is _____ units.

29. In the equation $b = (2 \times a) - 2$, what is the value of b if a is 14?

30. A computer costs $2290. An oven costs $\frac{1}{5}$ the cost of the computer. How much more does the computer cost than the oven?

---

31. A basket, together with 6 cans of mushrooms, weighs 3.05 lb. Each can of mushrooms weighs 0.43 lb. Find the weight of the basket when it is empty.

EXERCISE 1

1. Lisa carried out a survey among her friends to find their ages. She recorded the results in a tally chart.

Age	Number of friends
8	//
9	/////
10	///
11	//
12	/

(a) Organize the data beginning with the smallest.

8, 8, 9, _____, _____, _____, _____,

_____, _____, _____, _____,

_____, _____,

(b) Her youngest friends are _____ years old.

(c) Her oldest friend is _____ years old.

(d) The difference between the oldest and youngest is

_____ − _____ = _____ years.

(e) Her friends' median age is _____ years old.

2. Curtis scored the following points in his last 7 basketball games.

10, 14, 12, 13, 12, 12, 14

Record Curtis' scores on the line plot below.

(a) The least number of points Curtis scored is _____.

(b) The highest number of points Curtis scored is

_____.

(c) His median score is _____ points.

3. Juan carried out a survey among his friends to find out the numbers of siblings they have. He recorded the data on a line plot.

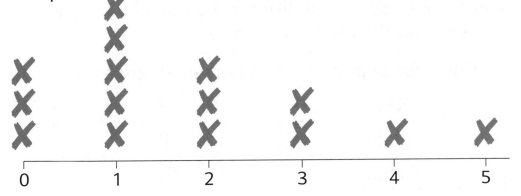

(a) Juan surveyed _____ friends.

(b) The highest number of siblings is _____.

(c) The lowest number of siblings is _____.

(d) The difference between the highest and lowest numbers of siblings is

_____ − _____ = _____.

(e) The median number of siblings is _____.

4. Simon measured the height of his friends and recorded the data in the table below.

Height in cm	150	145	152	143	149	138

(a) Organize the data from least to greatest.

_____

(b) What is the median height of his friends? _____

EXERCISE 2

1. The principal surveyed the students at school to find out
    which color they would like for the school uniforms.
    He recorded the results in a table.

Color for uniforms	Number of students
Red	73
Blue	110
Green	57
Black	44

    (a) Most students want the color _____ for
         their uniforms.

    (b) The color that the least number of students want is
         _____.

    (c) The mode of the data is the color _____.

2. Timothy recorded the number of cars, trucks and
    motorcycles that passed in front of his school in a
    one-hour period.
    He recorded the data in the table below.

Vehicle type	Number of vehicles
Car	21
Truck	6
Motorcycle	3

    (a) Most of the vehicles that passed by were _____.

    (b) The mode of the set of data is _____.

    (c) The type of vehicle that passed by the least was

         _____.

    (d) _____ more cars than trucks passed by.

    (e) _____ fewer motorcycles passed by than cars.

Unit 10: Data Analysis and Probability

EXERCISE 3

1. Araceli spinned a spinner and recorded the outcomes on a tally chart.

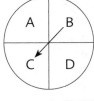

Section A	ⅢⅠ
Section B	||||
Section C	ⅢⅠ ||
Section D	||||

(a) The spinner landed on Section A _____ out of 20 times.

(b) The spinner landed on Section A $\dfrac{\boxed{}}{\boxed{20}} = \dfrac{\boxed{}}{\boxed{4}}$ of the time.

(c) The spinner landed on Section B _____ out of _____ times.

(d) The spinner landed on Section B $\dfrac{\boxed{4}}{\boxed{20}} = \dfrac{\boxed{1}}{\boxed{}}$ of the time.

(e) The spinner landed on Section C _____ out of _____ times.

(f) The spinner landed on Section C $\dfrac{\boxed{}}{\boxed{}}$ of the time.

(g) The spinner landed on Section D _____ out of _____ times.

(h) The spinner landed on Section D $\dfrac{\boxed{}}{\boxed{}} = \dfrac{\boxed{}}{\boxed{}}$ of the time.

2. Phillip rolled a regular six-sided die and recorded the results on the line plot below.

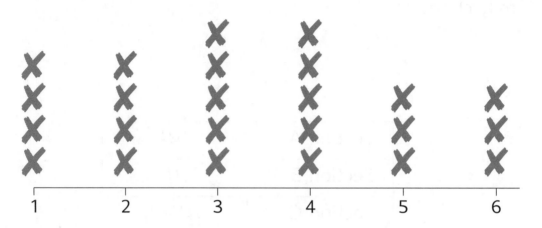

(a) Phillip rolled the die _____ times.

(b) He rolled a two _____ out of _____ times.

(c) He rolled a two $\frac{\square}{\square}$ of the time.

(d) He rolled a four _____ out of _____ times.

(e) He rolled a four $\frac{\square}{\square}$ of the time.

(f) He rolled a six _____ out of _____ times.

(g) He rolled a six $\frac{\square}{\square}$ of the time.

(h) He rolled a number less than three $\frac{\square}{\square}$ of the time.

EXERCISE 4

1. Rachel will toss a coin twice. Complete the tree diagram to show the different ways she might get heads and tails.

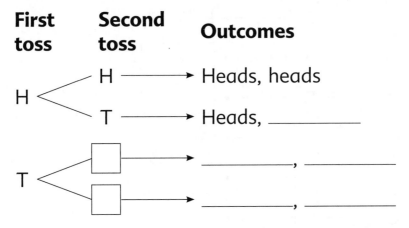

First toss	Second toss	Outcomes
H	H	Heads, heads
	T	Heads, _____
T	☐	_____ , _____
	☐	_____ , _____

There are _____ possible outcomes.

2. Sam spins the pointer three times. Complete the tree diagram to find the possible outcomes.

First spin	Second spin	Third spin	Outcomes
A	A	A	A, A, A
		B	A, A, B
		C	A, A, C
	B	A	A, B, A
		B	A, B, B
		C	A, B, C
	C	A	A, C, A
		B	A, C, B
		C	A, C, C

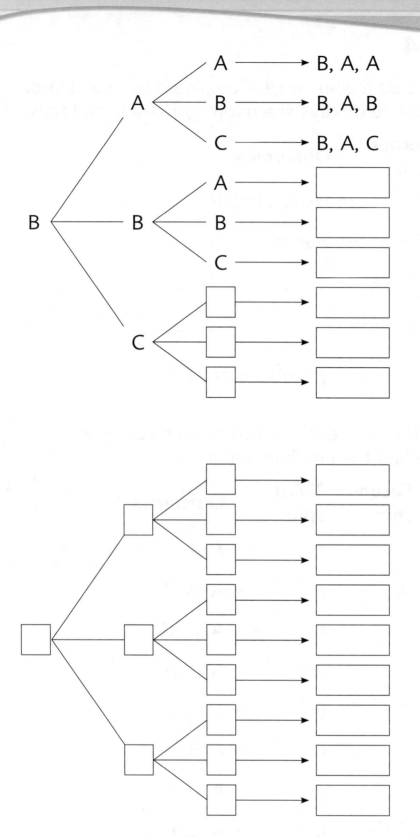

EXERCISE 5

1. The bar graph shows the number of cars sold by Mr. Wang in six months. Study the graph and answer the questions which follow.

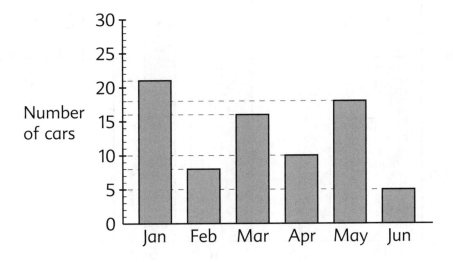

   (a) In which month did Mr. Wang sell the greatest number of cars? _____

   (b) In which month did he sell the smallest number of cars? _____

   (c) How many cars did he sell in May? _____

   (d) How many more cars did he sell in January than in April? _____

   (e) Find the total number of cars sold in the six months.

   _____

2. The bar graph shows the amount of money collected for two charities in four days. Study the graph and answer the questions which follow.

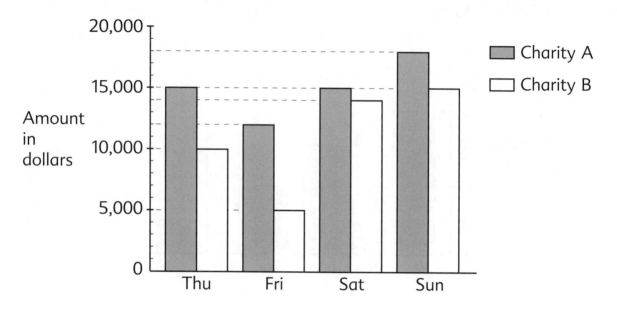

(a) How much money was collected on Sunday for each of the two charities?

_____

(b) On which day was the total amount of money collected greater than $30,000?

_____

(c) How much more money was collected for Charity A than for Charity B?

_____

(d) Express the amount of money collected on Friday as a fraction of the total amount of money collected in the four days.

_____

EXERCISE 6

1. The line graph shows the enrollment of a school for 4 years.
    Study the graph and answer the questions which follow.

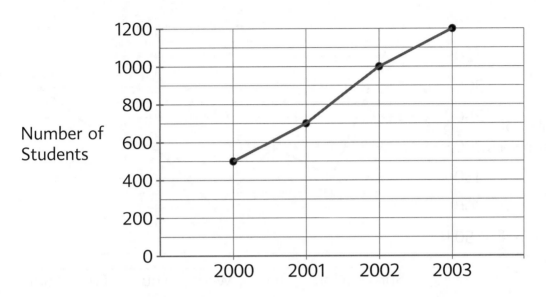

Number of Students

(a) What was the increase in enrollment from 2002
    to 2003?   _____

(b) When did the enrollment increase by 300 students
    in one year?   _____

(c) What was the difference between the enrollment
    in 2000 and the enrollment in 2003?   _____

(d) What was the total enrollment in the 4 years?

    _____

2. The line graph shows the daily sales of watermelons in a supermarket over a week. Study the graph and answer the questions which follow.

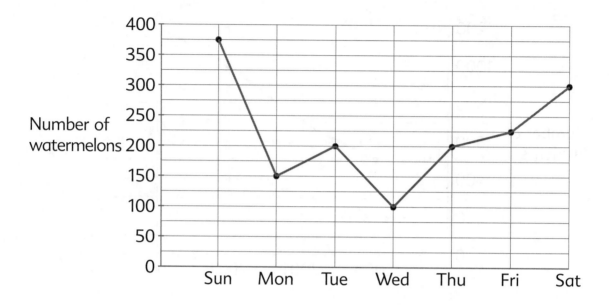

(a) On which day was the sales the lowest? _____

(b) What was the sales on Sunday? _____

(c) On which day were 300 watermelons sold? _____

(d) What was the increase in the sales from Friday to Saturday? _____

(e) When did the sales decrease by 100 in one day?

_____

3. The line graph shows the height of a plant measured at 8 a.m. every day for 5 days. Study the graph and answer the questions which follow.

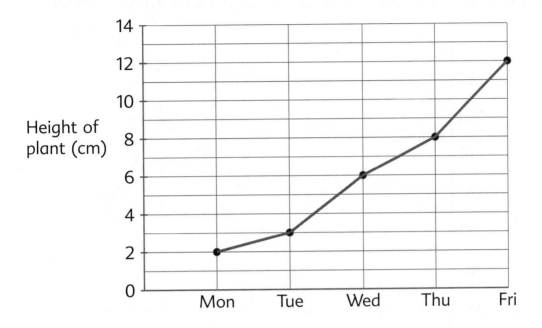

Height of plant (cm)

(a) What was the height of the plant measured on Tuesday? _____

(b) What was the increase in the height of the plant from Thursday to Friday? _____

(c) When did the plant grow by 3 cm in a day? _____

(d) When did the plant grow the fastest in a day? What was the increase in height? _____

(e) How many days did the plant take to grow from 2 cm to 12 cm? _____

4. The line graph shows the number of visitors in a park between 6:00 a.m. and 10:00 a.m. on a Sunday morning. Study the graph and answer the questions which follow.

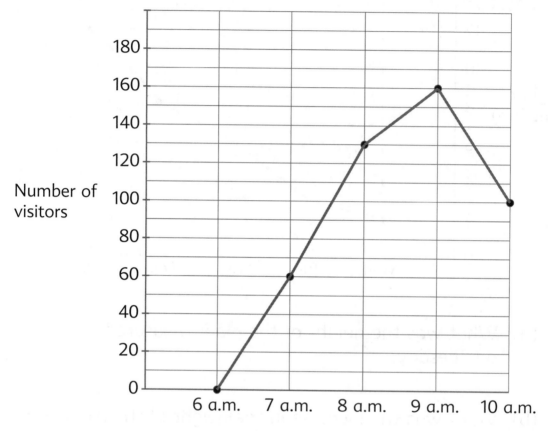

(a) At what time were there 60 visitors in the park?

_____

(b) How many visitors were there in the park at 8:00 a.m.?

_____

(c) When did the number of visitors increase by 30 in 1 hour?

_____

(d) When did the number of visitors increase the most in 1 hour?

_____

(e) When did the number of visitors decrease by 60 in 1 hour?

_____

EXERCISE 7

1. This graph shows the exchange rate between Hong Kong dollars and Singapore dollars in a certain year.

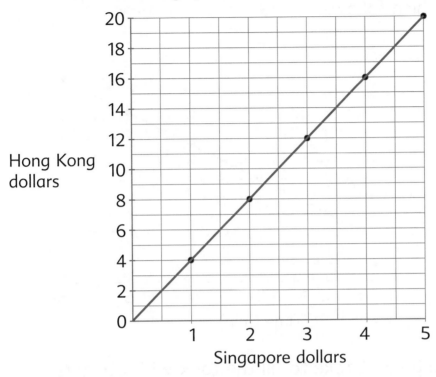

Study the graph and do the following.

(a)

Singapore dollars	1	2		4	
Hong Kong dollars			12		20

(b) Hong Kong $10 could be exchanged for Singapore $_____.

(c) Singapore $4.50 could be exchanged for Hong Kong $_____.

(d) Study the completed table in (a). Write an equation to show the relationship between Singapore dollars (s) and Hong Kong dollars (h).

    s = _____

(e) How many Singapore dollars could be exchanged for 100 Hong Kong dollars? _____

2. A tap was turned on for 6 minutes to fill a tank with water. The line graph shows the volume of water in the tank at the end of each minute. Study the graph and answer the questions which follow.

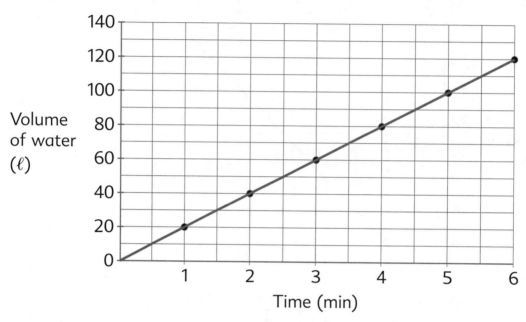

Volume of water (ℓ)

Time (min)

(a) How long did it take to fill the tank with 60 liters of water?

_____

(b) How long did it take to fill the tank with 90 liters of water?

_____

(c) How much water was in the tank at the end of 2 minutes?

_____

(d) How much water was in the tank at the end of $3\frac{1}{2}$ minutes?

_____

(e) (i) Complete the following.

Time (min)	1	2	3	4	5
Volume of water (ℓ)					

(ii) Write an equation to relate the volume of water (V) to the time (t).

$V =$ _____

REVIEW 10

1. Write the missing number in each of the following.

   (a) ☐ is 1000 more than 78,031.

   (b) ☐ is 1000 less than 56,100.

   (c) ☐ is 0.01 more than 23.28.

   (d) ☐ is 0.01 less than 18.22.

2. (a) In 32,105, which digit is in the
       hundreds place? _____

   (b) In 0.891, which digit is in the
       hundredths place? _____

3. (a) Round $35,465 to the nearest $100.   _____

   (b) Round 8.09 m to the nearest meter.   _____

   (c) Round 16.72 yd to the nearest yard.   _____

4. Complete the following regular number patterns.

   (a) $\frac{1}{6}$, $\frac{1}{3}$, $\frac{1}{2}$, ☐ , $\frac{5}{6}$, ☐

   (b) 2.75, 2.95, ☐ , ☐ , 3.55

   (c) 24, 20, 16, 12, 8, ☐ , ☐ , ☐ , ☐

5. Express $3\frac{5}{100}$ as a decimal.   _____

6. Which one of the following is equal to $\frac{2}{5}$?

   0.2, 0.4, 2.5, 0.25   _____

7. In a test, Matthew answered 32 out of 40 items correctly. What fraction of the items did he answer correctly?

   _____

8. David had $20. He spent $\frac{1}{10}$ of the money on lunch. How much did the lunch cost?

   _____

9. Draw a line parallel to PQ.

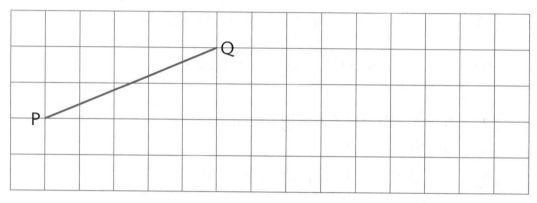

10. Draw an angle equal to 125°.

11. Complete the symmetric figure.
    (The dotted line is the line of symmetry.)
    Does the figure have rotational symmetry?   _____

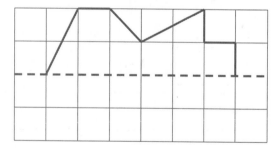

12. Elise can choose one of three flavors of yogurt; peach, vanilla or strawberry, and one of two toppings; chocolate sprinkles or nuts. How many different combinations can she choose from?

   _____

13. The pointer is spun twice, and the numbers added together. How many possible outcomes will have a sum greater than 4? _____

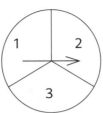

14. Which one of the following is a fraction in its simplest form?

$\dfrac{3}{9}$, $\dfrac{2}{10}$, $\dfrac{5}{7}$, $\dfrac{4}{8}$ _____

15. Express 2.4 as a fraction in its simplest form. _____

16. Find the value of each of the following.

(a) 6 + 0.6 + 0.06 _____

(b) 0.3 − 0.03 _____

(c) 4.8 × 5 _____

(d) 2.2 ÷ 4 _____

17. How many thirds are there in 3? _____

18. Divide 17 by 4.
Give the answer correct to 1 decimal place. _____

19. A television set cost $1800. It cost 4 times as much as a digital camera. Find the total cost of the television set and the digital camera. _____

20. After buying 2 shirts at $12.50 each, David had $39.85 left.

How much money did he have at first? _____

21. Sam spun a spinner that is divided into 6 equal sections labeled with the numbers 1 through 6. He recorded the results on a line plot.

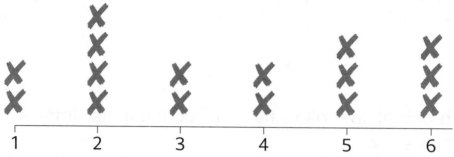

(a) How many times did Sam spin the spinner?

_____

(b) What fraction of the time did the spinner land on 2?

_____

(c) What fraction of the time did the spinner land on 4?

_____

(d) What fraction of the time did the spinner land on a number less than 4?

_____

(e) What fraction of the time did the spinner land on a number greater than 4?

_____

22. Larry rolls a regular six-sided die two times.

(a) Make a tree diagram showing all the possible outcomes.

(b) How many possible outcomes are there?   _____

23. Parallelogram ABCD has Vertex A at (2, 2), Vertex B at (2, 8), and Vertex C at (8, 9).

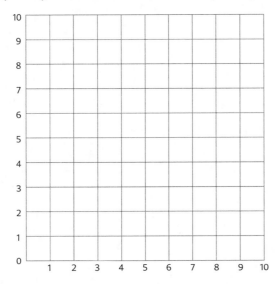

(a) What is the location of Vertex D? _____

(b) What are two parallel sides? _____

(c) What is the length of AB in units? _____

(d) Which two coordinates can we subtract to find the length of CD? _____

24. Reis received twice as much money as Ben. Ben received $14.80 less than Sam. If Sam received $61.20, how much money did Reis receive?

25. The area of a rectangle is 54 cm². The length of the rectangle is 9 cm. Find the perimeter of the rectangle.

26. Mrs. Jensen bought 4.5 ft of lace. She used 0.9 ft to make a dress. She used the rest to make 5 cushions of the same size. Find the length of lace she used to make each cushion.

27. After spending $\frac{3}{5}$ of his money on a tennis racket, Sean had $14 left. How much did the tennis racket cost?

EXERCISE 1

1. Fill in the blanks.

    (a) 25 m = _____ cm

    (b) 10 ft = _____ in.

    (c) 2 gal = _____ qt

    (d) 3 km = _____ m

    (e) 5 lb = _____ oz

    (f) 4 kg = _____ g

    (g) 6 ℓ = _____ ml

    (h) 11 days = _____ hr

2. Fill in the blanks.

    (a) 5 years 6 months = _____ months

    (b) 6 km 20 m = _____ m

    (c) 8 ℓ 100 ml = _____ ml

    (d) 5 ft 3 in. = _____ in.

    (e) 7 lb 15 oz = _____ oz

    (f) 4 kg 500 g = _____ g

    (g) 2 min 35 s = _____ s

    (h) 1 qt 1 pt = _____ pt

3. Fill in the blanks.

   (a) 30 months = _____ years _____ months

   (b) 101 cm = _____ m _____ cm

   (c) 70 min = _____ h _____ min

   (d) 30 oz = _____ lb _____ oz

   (e) 33 ft = _____ yd _____ ft

4. Add or subtract in compound units.

   (a) 3 hr 20 min + 6 hr 45 min = _____ hr _____ min

   (b) 12 kg 10 g − 10 kg 600 g = _____ kg _____ g

   (c) 17 ft 3 in. − 7 ft 4 in. = _____ ft _____ in.

   (d) 5 gal 2 qt + 1 gal 3 qt = _____ gal _____ qt

   (e) 11 lb 5 oz + 5 lb 11 oz = _____ lb _____ oz

EXERCISE 2

Fill in the blanks.

1. (a) 3 m 20 cm × 4 = _____ m _____ cm

    3 m   20 cm

    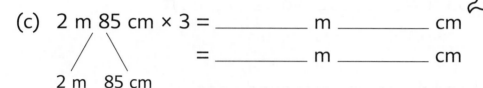
    Multiply the meters.
    Then multiply the centimeters.

   (b) 85 cm × 3 = _____ cm

        = _____ m _____ cm

   (c) 2 m 85 cm × 3 = _____ m _____ cm

        = _____ m _____ cm

    2 m   85 cm

2. (a) 2 ℓ 150 ml × 5 = _____ ℓ _____ ml

    2 ℓ   150 ml

   (b) 400 ml × 4 = _____ ml

        = _____ ℓ _____ ml

   (c) 3 ℓ 400 ml × 4 = _____ ℓ _____ ml

        = _____ ℓ _____ ml

    3 ℓ   400 ml

3. (a) 6 ft 2 in. × 4 = _____ ft _____ in.

    6 ft   2 in.

   (b) 9 in. × 6 = _____ in.

        = _____ ft _____ in.

   (c) 10 ft 9 in. × 6 = _____ ft _____ in.

        = _____ ft _____ in.

    10 ft   9 in.

Unit 11: Measures and Volume

4. A bottle holds 1 ℓ 500 ml of water. A bucket holds 3 times as much water as the bottle. How much water does the bucket hold?

_____

5. A washing machine takes 1 hour 40 minutes to wash one load of laundry. How long does it take to wash 4 loads of laundry?

_____

6. A fruit seller packed all his oranges into 6 boxes. Each box of oranges weighed 12 lb 12 oz. What was the total weight of the oranges?

EXERCISE 3

Fill in the blanks.

1. (a) 4 km 250 m ÷ 2 = _____ km _____ m

     4 km   250 m

> Divide the kilometers.
> Then divide the meters.

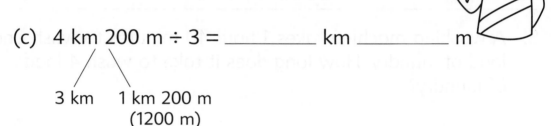

  (b) 1 km 200 m ÷ 3 = 1200 m ÷ 3

                    = _____ m

  (c) 4 km 200 m ÷ 3 = _____ km _____ m

     3 km   1 km 200 m
            (1200 m)

2. (a) 6 h 45 min ÷ 3 = _____ h _____ min

     6 h   45 min

  (b) 1 h 20 min ÷ 4 = 80 min ÷ 4

                    = _____ min

  (c) 5 h 20 min ÷ 4 = _____ h _____ min

     4 h   1 h 20 min
           (80 min)

3. Meredith had 6 lb 12 oz of mushrooms. She packed them equally into 9 boxes. What was the weight of the mushrooms in each box?

4. Johnny had 4 m 50 cm of wire. He cut the wire equally into 3 pieces. He used 2 pieces of the wire to repair his toy.

   (a) How long was each piece of wire?
   (b) What length of wire did he use to repair his toy?

5. A box containing 5 identical books weighs 6 kg 850 g. If the weight of the box is 600 g, what is the weight of each book?

EXERCISE 4

1. The following solids are made up of 1-cm cubes.
    What is the volume of each solid?

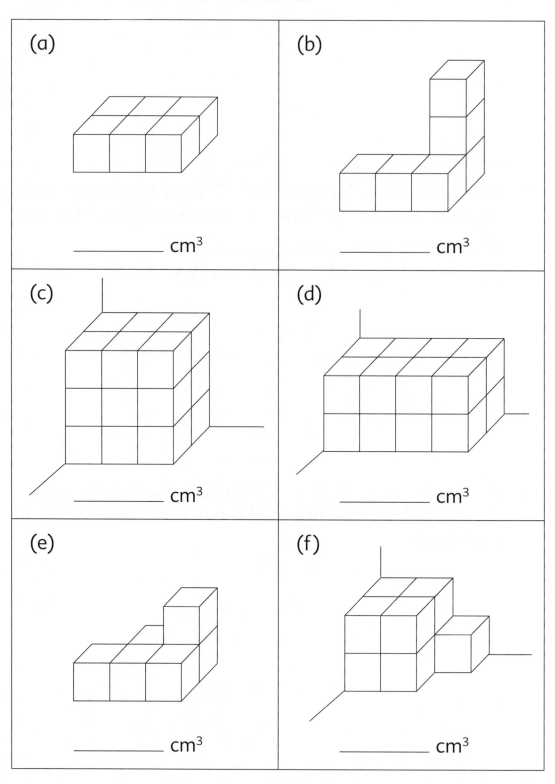

(a) _____ cm³

(b) _____ cm³

(c) _____ cm³

(d) _____ cm³

(e) _____ cm³

(f) _____ cm³

EXERCISE 5

1. These solids are made up of 1-in. cubes.

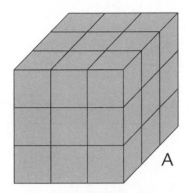

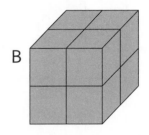

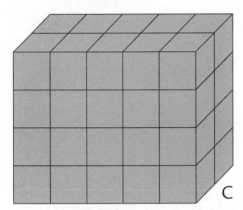

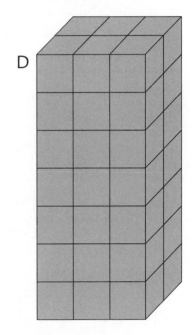

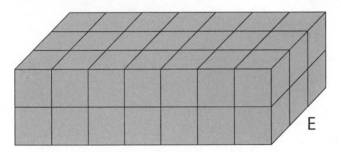

Complete the following table.

Solid	Length	Width	Height	Volume
A	3 in.	3 in.	3 in.	27 in.³
B				
C				
D				
E				

2. Find the volume of each rectangular prism.

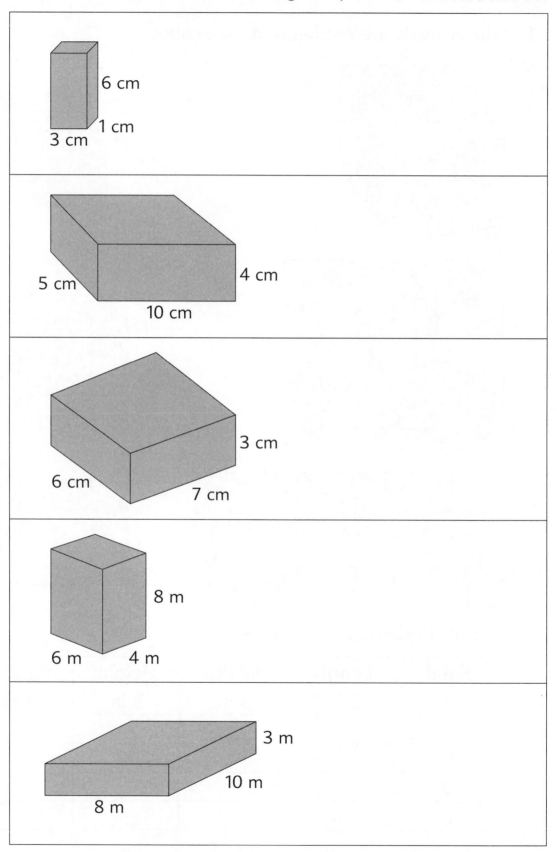

EXERCISE 6

1. Write the volume of the water in cubic centimeters.
    (1 ℓ = 1000 cm³)

    (a)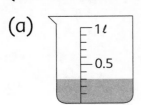

    _____ cm³

    (b)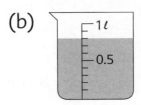

    _____ cm³

2. Find the volume of the water in milliliters. (1 ml = 1 cm³)

    (a)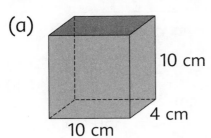

    _____ ml

    (b)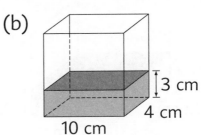

    _____ ml

3. Find the volume of the water in liters. (1 ℓ = 1000 cm³)

    (a)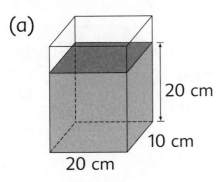

    _____ ℓ

    (b)

    _____ ℓ

4. Find the volume of the water in liters and milliliters.

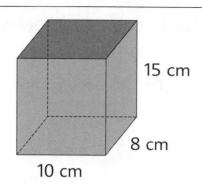

15 cm

8 cm

10 cm

The volume of the water
is _____.

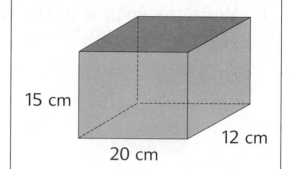

15 cm

20 cm

12 cm

The volume of the water
is _____.

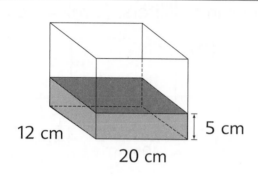

12 cm

20 cm

5 cm

The volume of the water
is _____.

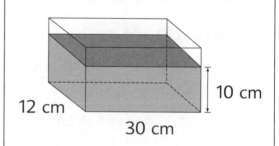

12 cm

30 cm

10 cm

The volume of the water
is _____.

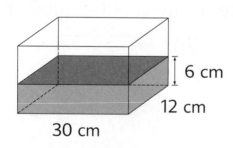

6 cm

12 cm

30 cm

The volume of the water
is _____.

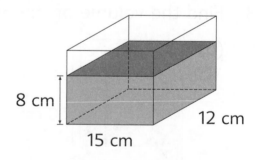

8 cm

15 cm

12 cm

The volume of the water
is _____.

REVIEW 11

1. Arrange the following in order, beginning with the greatest.
   2 m 35 cm,   253 cm,   2 km,   20 m

   _____

2. Write the missing number in each of the following.

   (a) The digit **8** in **58**,270 stands for 8 × _____.

   (b) The digit **5** in 48.**5**2 stands for 5 × _____.

3. Write 4 tens 6 tenths as a decimal.   _____

4. (a) What number is 0.1 more than 5.9?   _____

   (b) What number is 2 more than −2?   _____

5. (a) Write down **all** the factors of 20.

   _____

   (b) Write down **all** the common factors of 12 and 16.

   _____

   (c) What are the prime numbers between 1 and 10?

   _____

6. Estimate the sum of 3548, 497 and 9621 by first
   rounding each number to the nearest hundred.   _____

7. Round 147.25 lb to 1 decimal place.   _____

8. Which one of the following is the greatest?
   4.2,   4.3,   4.23,   4.32   _____

9. Which one of the following is the smallest?
   $\frac{5}{4}$, $\frac{1}{2}$, $\frac{3}{4}$, $\frac{3}{8}$ _____

10. Which one of the following is the same as $1\frac{1}{2}$?
    1.1,   1.2,   1.5,   2.2   _____

11. Write the missing number in each of the following.

(a) 2 km 634 m = _____ m

(b) 5 kg 107 g = _____ g

(c) 3 h 4 min = _____ min

(d) 260 min = _____ h _____ min

(e) 4007 g = _____ kg _____ g

(f) 580 cm = _____ m _____ cm

(g) 3020 ml = _____ ℓ _____ ml

(h) 108 oz = _____ lb _____ oz

12. A carton contains 250 ml of fruit juice. How much fruit juice can you get from 6 such cartons? Give your answer in liters and milliliters. _____

13. A pineapple weighs 1 kg 680 g. A papaya is 800 g lighter than the pineapple. Find the total weight of the two fruits. _____

14. Alice bought 6 ft of lace. She used 1 ft 3 in. of lace for a dress. She used 1 ft 8 in. of lace for another dress. How much lace did she have left? _____

15. Jamie bought 6 identical dictionaries as prizes for some party games. The total weight of the dictionaries was 7 lb 8 oz. What was the weight of each dictionary? _____

16. A watermelon weighs 2 kg 450 g. A pineapple weighs 865 g. How much heavier is the watermelon than the pineapple? _____

17. Draw a line parallel to AB.

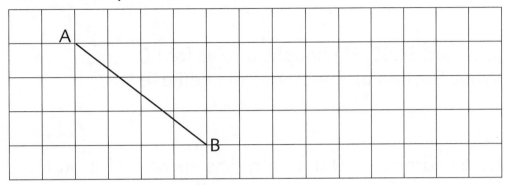

18. Write the missing number in each of the following.

(a) 385 ml × 4 is equal to _____ ℓ _____ ml.

(b) 3 km 650 m is equal to _____ m.

19. The amount of water in the jug can fill 3 glasses. What is the capacity of each glass?

_____

20. Mr. Morrison made 6 plant holders. He used 3.82 m of wire for each plant holder. How many meters of wire did he use altogether? _____

21. Casey cut a wire 8 ft long into 6 equal pieces. How many feet long is each piece? (Give the answer correct to 1 decimal place.) _____

22.

Shrimp	$1.50 per 100 g
Fish	$4.50 per kg

Mrs. Goldberg bought 500 g of shrimp and 1 kg of fish.
How much did she spend altogether? _____

23. John had $1.50. He bought a ruler for 50 cents.
What fraction of the money did he have left? _____

24. Karen earned $840 a month. She spent $\frac{2}{5}$ of it on food.
How much did she spend on food? _____

25. Gene walked 5 times around a rectangular field
measuring 45 yd by 20 yd. How many yards did he
walk altogether?

26. The figure shows a solid that is
made up of 1-cm cubes.
What is the volume of the solid?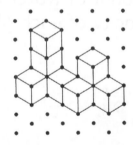

_____

27. A tank measures 15 m by 6 m by 5 m. It is filled with water
to a depth of 4 m. How much water is there in the tank?
Give the answer in cubic meters.

_____

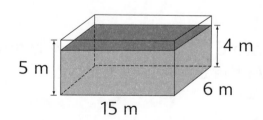

5 m
4 m
6 m
15 m

28. A picture measures 30 cm by 24 cm. It is mounted on a rectangular card leaving a margin of 3 cm around it. Find the perimeter of the card.

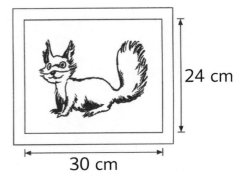

24 cm

30 cm

---

29. Alan used $\frac{3}{4}$ of his money to buy a watch which cost $45. How much money did he have left?

30. A tank can hold 30.1 gal of water. A bucket can hold $\frac{1}{7}$ as much water as the tank. Find the capacity of the bucket.

31. The perimeter of a rectangle is 30 in. The width of the rectangle is half its length. Find the area of the rectangle.

32. Neil saved 15 quarters in January. He saved 35 nickels in February. He saved 21 dimes in March. How much money did he save in the three months?

_____

33. How many quarters are there in $116.75?

_____

34. Show all the possible outcomes for the gender (boy or girl) of three children in a family.

35. Juan asked his friends how many hours a week they spent doing homework and recorded the data in a tally chart.

Hours spent on homework	Number of friends
5	//
6	
7	///
8	///
9	//
10	//
12	/

(a) Make a line plot to show the data.

(b) What is the fewest number of hours Juan's friends spent on homework? _____

(c) What is the greatest number of hours Juan's friends spent on homework? _____

(d) What is the median number of hours Juan's friends spent on homework? _____

(e) How many hours do most of Juan's friends spend on homework (the mode)? _____

36. Mary flips a coin 4 times.
    (a) Make a tree diagram to show the different ways she can get heads and tails.
    (b) How many possible outcomes are there?

Blank